Together We Sing

by
IRVING WOLFE
Head, Division of Music, George Peabody College for Teachers
Nashville, Tennessee

and
MARGARET FULLERTON
Iowa State Teacher's College, Cedar Falls, Iowa

Based on the original work of
CHARLES A. FULLERTON

ILLUSTRATIONS *by* MARY GEHR

All-Grades Edition

Follett Publishing Company   CHICAGO   *New York   Los Angeles*

ACKNOWLEDGEMENT is due to the following publishers and individuals for their generous permission to use copyrighted material: to the Milton Bradley Company, Springfield, Mass., for the melody for "Bean Porridge Hot"; to Robbins Music Corporation, New York, for their arrangement of "Caisson Song"; to Carl Fischer, Inc., New York, for "Cindy"; to Danish American Young People's League for "The Crafty Crow" from *A World of Song*, copyright, 1941; to Laidlaw Brothers, Chicago, for the following songs from the Bentley Song Series: "The Fiddle," "My Old Dan," "Soldier Boys," "Dancing We Go," "The Bee," "Who Has Seen the Wind?" "Honk! Honk!" "Cradle Song," "Wing Foo," "The Zoo," "The Seasons"; to G. Ricordi and Company, New York, for the H. T. Burleigh arrangement of "Deep River," copyright, 1917; to Lulu W. Hale, Ary, Ky., for her version of "Down in the Valley"; to the Presbyterian Board of Christian Education for their arrangement of the music to "Finlandia," and also for the words to "We Would Be Building," copyright, 1936 by Purd E. Dietz; to Lynn Rohrbaugh, Co-operative Recreation Service, Delaware, O., for the play-party games "Skip to M' Lou," "Paw Paw Patch," and "Captain Jinks"; to the H. W. Gray Company, New York, for "Frog Went A-Courting" from *Lonesome Tunes;* to the League of Nations Association, Inc., for the words to "Hymn for the Nations," copyright, 1934; to Janet E. Tobitt for "Kookaburra" from *The Ditty Bag*, copyright, 1946; to Scott, Foresman & Company, Chicago, for the following songs from the *Lyric Music Series:* "Popcorn," "The Railroad Train," "God's Gifts," "Japanese Parasol," "Sun and Stars," "Good Morning," "A True Story," "Christmas Hymn," "The Echo," "The Honeybee," "The Music Box," "Company," "The Brooklet," "Sailor Lads," "The First Tulip," "Follow On," "The Sailboat," "Mystic Number," "Frog Music," "Crystal Day"; to the U.S. Marine Corps for "Marines' Hymn"; to the Harvard University Press for "Short'nin' Bread" from *On the Trail of Negro Folk Song*, by Dorothy Scarborough, copyright, 1925; to L. L. McDowell, Smithville, Tenn., for "Shuckin' of the Corn"; to the Theodore Presser Company, Philadelphia, for the four measures from "The Stars and Stripes Forever," published and copyrighted by the John Church Company, and also for the following songs from *Songs of the Child World* by Riley and Gaynor, copyright, 1897, by the John Church Company: "Tracks in the Snow," "Brownies," "Sweet Pea Ladies," and "The Little Shoemaker"; to the Century Music Publishing Company, New York, for their version of "There Stands a Little Man" and "Susy, Little Susy"; to Charles Scribner's Sons, New York, for the poem by M. D. Babcock, "This Is My Father's World," and also for the use of the following songs from Farnsworth's *Grammer School Songs:* "The Tailor and the Mouse," "My Banjo," "The Frog and the Mouse," "Wraggle Taggle Gypsies," and "Weel May the Keel Row"; to G. A. Grant-Schaefer for "Song of the Cricket" and "My Pony," copyright, 1923; to Doris White for "Three Little Girls" from *Physical Education for Elementary Schools* by Monica R. Wild and Doris E. White, published by Iowa State Teachers College, Cedar Falls, Ia.; to Hampton Institute, Hampton, Va., for the arrangements of "Nobody Knows the Trouble I See" and "Lord, I Want To Be a Christian"; to Ruby Terrill Lomax for "Little Bird, Go Thru My Window" from *Our Singing Country* by John and Alan Lomax; to the Bureau of American Ethnology for "We-We-We," reprinted by their permission from *Chippewa Music* by Frances Densmore, Bulletin 45; to the Macmillan Company for "High, Betty Martin" from *Folk Songs of Old New England* by Eloise Linscott, copyright, 1939, by the publishers and used with their permission; to Boosey & Hawkes, Inc., New York, N. Y., for the theme from "Pomp and Circumstance" by Sir Edward Elgar.

CONTENTS

NOTE TO TEACHERS

For best results the teacher should make constant use of the following materials:

1. THE TEACHER'S GUIDE *for* TOGETHER WE SING
2. FOLLETT EDUCATIONAL RECORDS (*See pages 256-258*)
3. CLASSIFIED INDEX (*See pages 259-264*)

Figures under song titles throughout the book indicate record numbers in the FOLLETT EDUCATIONAL RECORD SERIES.

OUR MUSIC

We are glad you have a book of songs like this to use in school and at home. It will bring you many hours of shared enjoyment with others who love to sing. We hope you will have other good books of songs, too, and many beautiful recordings to help you become acquainted with the fascinating world of music.

In one sense what we see on these pages is not really *music* until we *sing* it or *play* it or *hear* it. By so doing we make it live again. That is why it is so important to do it well. And each time we succeed truly well, we feel a very real pleasure, because the result is music that *we* have re-created. It is *our music!*

TO SHARE IS TO BE RICHER

When we have really enjoyed our music, we want to share that fine experience with others. If we divide our money or our food with someone else, we have less for ourselves. But with music, the more we give the more we have.

We want to know the songs and games of children who live in other parts of our country and in other lands far away. When we know their songs and they know ours, we feel better acquainted than before; and that leads to friendly understanding and more helpful co-operation. Both understanding and co-operation are very important in our community, in our country, and in a world of friendly, helpful neighbors.

So let's *share* our music—at home, with other groups at school, with groups from neighboring schools! *Sing together! Play together! Listen together!*

Popcorn
(101B)

Rather quickly

SING · LISTEN

1. Oh, just 'round the cor-ner, a man dressed in white
2. It looks just like snow, but it's all pip-ing hot;

SING · LISTEN

Sells hot roast-ed pop-corn from morn-ing till night.
It pops like tor-pe-does and rat-tles like shot.

SING

"Fresh pop-corn! Pop-corn!"
"Fresh pop-corn! Pop-corn!"

LISTEN · SING

Five cents will buy a lit-tle bag, salt-ed just right.
Who has a nick-el or a dime? I'd like a lot!

Mother Goose Lullaby

Quickly

GERMAN MELODY

LISTEN

SING

Hush-a-bye, ba-by, thy cra-dle is green; Fa-ther's a
Do re mi fa sol mi sol fa re fa mi Do re mi fa

LISTEN

no-ble-man, Moth-er's a queen; Sis-ter's a la-dy and wears a gold
sol mi sol fa re ti do Do do do ti sol sol la ti do

SING slowing

ring; Broth-er's a drum-mer and drums for the king.
sol Fa fa fa mi mi mi re do re do

From *The Modern Music Series*, by permission of Silver Burdett Co., New York, owners of the copyright.

The Bee

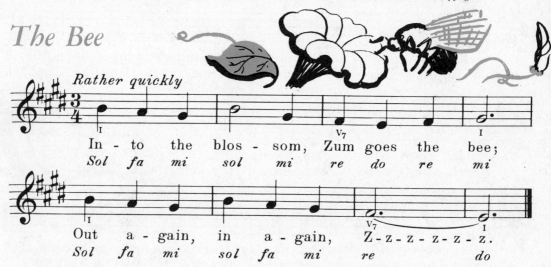

Rather quickly

In-to the blos-som, Zum goes the bee;
Sol fa mi sol mi re do re mi

Out a-gain, in a-gain, Z-z-z-z-z-z.
Sol fa mi sol fa mi re do

2

Diddle, Diddle, Dumpling
(201B)

MOTHER GOOSE

ETHEL CROWNINSHIELD
Acc. by I.W.

SING
Playfully

Did - dle, did - dle, dump - ling, my son John,

LISTEN   SING

Went to bed with his stock-ings on; One shoe off and

LISTEN

one shoe on, Did - dle, did - dle dump - ling, my son John.

Bobby Shafto
(201A)

MOTHER GOOSE

OLD ENGLISH TUNE

Gaily LISTEN   SING

1. Bob-by Shaf-to's gone to sea! Sil - ver buck-les on his knee;
2. Bob-by Shaf-to's fat and fair, Comb-ing down his yel-low hair;

LISTEN   SING

He'll come back and mar - ry me, Pret-ty Bob-by Shaf-to!
He's my love for - ev - er-more, Pret-ty Bob-by Shaf-to!

3

Pussy-Cat, Pussy-Cat

MOTHER GOOSE

J. W. ELLIOTT

Quickly, with two pulses per measure

LISTEN
Puss - y - cat, puss - y - cat, where have you been?

SING
I've been to Lon - don to vis - it the queen.

LISTEN
Puss - y - cat, puss - y - cat, what did you there? I

fright - en'd a lit - tle mouse un - der her chair!

Jack and Jill
(401A)

MOTHER GOOSE
Playfully

J. W. ELLIOTT

LISTEN   SING
1. Jack and Jill went up the hill to fetch a pail of wa - ter;
2. Up Jack got and home did trot as fast as he could ca - per;

LISTEN   SING
Jack fell down and broke his crown, and Jill came tumb-ling aft-er.
Went to bed to mend his head with vine-gar and brown pa-per.

4

Dancing We Go
(401B)

With light movement   ALYS BENTLEY

LISTEN   SING

One, two, three, one, two, three, Danc - ing we go,

LISTEN   SING

One, two, three, one, two, three, All on tip - toe.

Honk! Honk!
(201A)

Gaily   ALYS BENTLEY

SING   LISTEN

Honk! honk! In my mo - tor car. All a - round the

world we go, Ver - y fast or ver - y slow.

SING

Honk! honk! In my mo - tor car.

Honk! honk, honk!

Ride a Cock Horse to Banbury Cross

(201A)

MOTHER GOOSE

J. W. ELLIOTT

Fast, with two bounds per measure

Ride a cock-horse to Ban-bur-y Cross,

To see a fine la-dy up-on a white horse;

Rings on her fin-gers and bells on her toes,

She shall have mu-sic wher-ev-er she goes.

No pedal

6

I Love Little Pussy

MOTHER GOOSE

J. W. ELLIOTT
Acc. by I.W.

With a gentle pulse

SING

I love lit-tle puss-y, her coat is so warm,

LISTEN

And if I don't hurt her, she'll do me no harm.

SING

I'll sit by the fire and give her some food,

LISTEN

And puss-y will love me be-cause I am good.

Little Jack Horner
(301A)

MOTHER GOOSE

J. W. ELLIOTT
Acc. by I.W.

Quickly, in fun

Lit-tle Jack Hor-ner sat in a cor-ner, Eat-ing a Christ-mas pie, ___

LISTEN

He put in his thumb and pulled out a plum

SING *Slower*

And said, "What a good boy am I!" ___

My Old Dan
(301A)

RON CRAIGHILL

MAX LOWEN

SING — LISTEN

With a steady trot

Jog, jog, jog, jog, My old Dan is al-ways read-y;
Loud soft soft soft Loud — soft — soft — soft —

Jog, jog, jog, jog, Slow he is but kind and stead-y;
Loud soft soft soft Loud — soft — soft — soft —

Jog, jog, jog, jog, When I want to I can stop him
Loud soft soft soft Loud — soft — soft — soft —

Just by say-ing, "Whoa!" "Whoa!"
Loud — soft — soft soft Loud-soft-soft-soft

Can you clap the regular pulse of this song? The
words, "Loud soft soft soft," are written in to help you.

The Japanese Parasol
(201B)

NETTIE RYLE   Acc. by I. W.

Brightly

SING / LISTEN

I had a pret-ty par-a-sol, Long, long a-go,

SING / LISTEN

A fun-ny Jap-an-es-y one Tied with a bow.

SING / LISTEN

'Twas on-ly made of pa-per tho', Just for pre-tend;

retard *slowly*

SING / LISTEN

I took it in the rain one day, That was the end!

11

Sun and Stars

With spirit

SING ... LISTEN

1. Sun wakes up at morn - ing And goes to bed at eve - ning.
2. Stars wake up at eve - ning And go to bed at morn - ing.
Do sol do mi sol mi do re mi re do ti sol

SING ... LISTEN

Sun wakes up at morn - ing And brings us light.
Stars wake up at eve - ning And play all night.
Do sol do mi sol mi do re sol do

12

An Easy Song

(101A)

GERMAN FOLK SONG

Lightly

LISTEN   SING

1. Cuck-oo,   cuck-oo,
2. Cuck-oo,   cuck-oo!
3. *Sol   mi   sol   mi*

LISTEN

Don't try to hide from me;
It's such an eas-y song;
I hear the cuck-oo say.

SING

Cuck-oo,   cuck-oo,
Cuck-oo,   cuck-oo!
Sol   mi   sol   mi

LISTEN

I see you in the tree.
It's hard to get it wrong.
I think it's here to stay.

13

MOTHER GOOSE

Sing a Song of Sixpence

(201B)

J. W. ELLIOTT
Acc. by I.W.

SING
Lightly

1.   Sing a song of six - pence, A pock-et full of rye;
2. The king was in the count-ing house   Count-ing out his mon-ey;

LISTEN

Four and twen-ty black-birds Baked   in   a pie.
The queen was in the par - lor   Eat-ing bread and hon-ey;

SING

When the pie was o - pened, The birds be-gan to sing;
The maid was in the gar - den   Hang-ing out the clothes,

LISTEN

Was - n't that a dain-ty dish To   set be-fore the king?
A - long   came a black - bird And snipped off her nose!

Our voices sound best when we sing *easily*.

14

Mary Had a Little Lamb

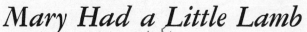

SARAH J. HALE   *Kay of F*   TRADITIONAL *fled*

1. Mar-y had a lit-tle lamb, Lit-tle lamb, lit-tle lamb;
2. And ev-'ry-where that Mar-y went, Mar-y went, Mar-y went; And
3. It fol-lowed her to school one day, School one day, school one day; It
4. It made the chil-dren laugh and play, Laugh and play, laugh and play; It

Mar-y had a lit-tle lamb, Its fleece was white as snow.
ev-'ry-where that Mar-y went, The lamb was sure to go.
fol-lowed her to school one day, Which was a-gainst the rule.
made the chil-dren laugh and play, To see a lamb at school.

Bean Porridge Hot

MOTHER GOOSE   ETHEL CROWNINSHIELD

Quickly, in fun

Bean por-ridge hot,   Bean por-ridge cold,

Bean por-ridge in the pot nine days old.   Some like it hot,

Some like it cold,   Some like it in the pot   Nine days old.

15

The Fiddle
(301A)

HYLAS IRISH · ALETA ROSSITER

Very smoothly

LISTEN · SING

Draw the bow a - cross the string, Hm — — m,
Mi mi sol sol fa mi re do re mi do

LISTEN · SING

Lis - ten to my fid - dle sing, Hm — m.
Mi mi sol sol fa mi re do do

Ten Little Indians

SING · LISTEN

1. One lit-tle, two lit-tle, three lit-tle In-dians, Four lit-tle,
2. Ten lit-tle, nine lit-tle, eight lit-tle In-dians, Sev'n lit-tle,

SING

five lit-tle, six lit-tle In - dians, Sev'n lit-tle, eight lit-tle,
six lit-tle, five lit-tle In - dians, Four lit-tle, three lit-tle,

LISTEN

nine lit-tle In-dians, Ten lit-tle In-dian boys. (girls)
two lit-tle In-dians, One lit-tle In-dian boy. (girl)

Directions: While singing the first stanzas, the children appear suddenly —one by one—walking Indian fashion. In the second stanza, they disappear one by one.

16

The Echo

(201A)

KATE FORMAN

OLD CHILDREN'S AIR

Espressivo (with expression)

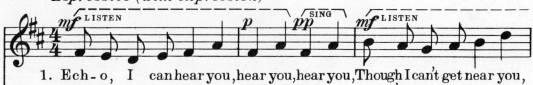

1. Ech-o, I can hear you, hear you, hear you, Though I can't get near you,
2. Now the rain is fall-ing, fall-ing, fall-ing, So I'll stop my call-ing,
3. First it's say-ing *mi sol mi sol mi sol* Then re-peat-ing *la do*

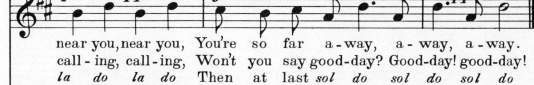

near you, near you, You're so far a-way, a-way, a-way.
call-ing, call-ing, Won't you say good-day? Good-day! good-day!
la do la do Then at last *sol do sol do sol do*

Cradle Song
(201B)

ROSE CRAIGHILL

Acc. by Harvey Worthington Loomis

Not slowly

SING / LISTEN

Bye - low, bye - low, Ba - by's in the cra - dle sleep - ing,

SING / LISTEN

Tip - toe, tip - toe, Still as puss - y sly - ly creep - ing,

Tracks in the Snow

ALICE C. D. RILEY   JESSIE L. GAYNOR

Quickly, with excitement

LISTEN
Do you see these ti - ny tracks in the snow?

SING
Don't you won - der what they are, where they go?

LISTEN
I think a Bun - ny Rab - bit white

SING
Has hopped a - cross the snow last night,

LISTEN
Oh! what fun - ny lit - tle tracks in the snow!

Song of the Seasons
(201A)

ROBERT LOUIS STEVENSON
Second Stanza by G. E.

ALETA ROSSITER

Smoothly

SING

1. Sing a song of sea-sons,
2. Spark-ling snow in win-ter,

Do re mi fa sol do

LISTEN

Some-thing bright in all
Bird-songs in the spring;

la do ti la sol

SING

Flow-ers in the sum-mer,
Gifts of Moth-er Na-ture

Do re mi fa sol sol

LISTEN

Fires in the fall.
Bright-en ev-'ry-thing.

re fa mi re do

21

The Honeybee
(201B)

KATE FORMAN

Easily, but not slowly

LISTEN

Mi	mi	re	mi	sol	sol	fa	fa
1. I	heard	a	lit - tle	hon - ey - bee;			
2. She	whis - pered	to	a	fra - grant	bloom,		
3. The	blos - som	o - pened	wide	its	door,		
4. I'm	sure	this	lit - tle	bee will	meet,		

fa	fa	mi	fa	la	la	sol	sol
"The	flow'rs	are	ver - y	sweet,"	said	she,	
"You've	some - thing	sweet - er	than	per - fume,			
She	tip - toed	on	the	crim - son	floor;		
In	ev - 'ry	flow'r	a	hon - ey	treat;		

sol	sol	sol	sol	sol	sol	sol	sol
"I	love	them	all,	zum	zum	zum	zum,
Please	let	me	see,	zum	zum	zum	zum,
"How	ver - y	kind,	zum	zum	zum	zum,	
"O	please,"	and	"thank	you,"	zum	zum	zum,

SING

sol	la	ti	do
And	all	love	me."
Your	hon - ey	room."	
I'll	have	some	more."
Will	make	life	sweet.

22

The Singing School
(301B)

KATE FORMAN

GERMAN FOLK TUNE
Acc. by I.W.

SING · LISTEN · *Joyfully*

1. Tra la la la la, O hear the swal - low,
2. Tra la la la la, the trees are swing - ing,
3. Tra la la la la, the wind is spring - ing,

SING · LISTEN

Tra la la la la, he calls us long;
Tra la la la la, the grape - vines too;
Tra la la la la, with - in the wood:

SING · LISTEN

"Hap - py lit - tle chil - dren, come and fol - low,
Ev - 'ry lit - tle blue - bell ring - ing, ring - ing,
Here's the ver - y school for sing - ing, sing - ing,

SING · LISTEN

Here's the ver - y place to learn a lit - tle song."
Marks the mer - ry time for teach - ing me and you.
Learn - ing to be glad and learn - ing to be good.

23

Hobby Horse
(101A)

C. HAHN

C. G. HERING
Acc. by I. W.

Lively

1. Trot, trot, trot! Go, and nev-er stop; Where'tis smooth and
2. Hey, hey, hey! Go a-long, I say! Do not kick and
Do mi sol sol fa mi re do Bits of tune like

where 'tis ston-y, Trudge a-long, my lit-tle po-ny;
do not stum-ble, Do not tire and do not grum-ble;
this are com-mon, Lis-ten well, we'll hear them of-ten,

Go and nev-er stop. Trot, trot, trot, trot, trot!
Go a-long I say. Hey, hey, hey, hey, hey!
Do re mi fa sol sol fa mi re do

The Farmer in the Dell

(301B)

LISTEN   SING

1. The farm-er in the dell, The farm-er in the dell,
Sol do do do do do do mi mi mi mi mi

LISTEN

Heigh o! the der-ry oh,
sol sol la sol mi do

dim. SING

The farm-er in the dell.
re mi mi re re do

2. The farmer takes a wife etc.
3. The wife takes the child etc.
4. The child takes the nurse etc.
5. The nurse takes the dog etc.
6. The dog takes the cat etc.
7. The cat takes the rat etc.
8. The rat takes the cheese etc.
9. The cheese stands alone etc.

25

CHRISTINA ROSSETTI

A Sure Sign
(401A)

I.W.

Look at the clouds, Com - ing in crowds!

See how much dark - er it grows!

We shall have rain, That's ver - y plain,

I felt a drop on my nose!

The Railroad Train
(101A)

From "Jolly Jingles"   CHARLES HARVEY

Allegro (quick)

LISTEN

1. Click - et - y clack, a - lunk, a - lunk!
2. O - ver the bridge, a - cross the lake,

SING

A train is com - ing, a - chunck, a - chunck;
A mile a min - ute it has to make—

LISTEN

A click - et - y clack a mile a - way;
A ter - ri - ble snake, with flam - ing eyes,

SING

It has - n't a sec - ond o' time to stay;
That wig - gles and wrig - gles a - long the ties.

LISTEN

It sings a nois - y clack - et - y song,
The cin - ders fall in fi - er - y rain—

SING

A rick - et - y, rock - et - y, rack - et - y song,—
A tun - nel is wait - ing to swal - low the train—

LISTEN

"You're on the track; get out o' the way, go 'long!"
Good - bye, good - bye! to - mor - row he'll come a - gain!

27

The Squirrel

ADA I. VOSE

GERMAN FOLK SONG

Gaily

LISTEN   SING

1. You may not think the squir-rel Of whom you some-times sing,
2. But if you go a - nut-ting Some chil-ly au-tumn day,

Do do mi do mi sol mi do sol do sol do sol

LISTEN   SING

Who seems so fond of play-ing, E'er works at an-y-thing.
You'll find that Mas-ter Squir-rel, Can work as well as play.

Sol fa re re fa mi do mi re fa ti re do

From *The Modern Music Series*, by permission of Silver Burdett Co., New York, owners of the copyright.

Little Bo-Peep
(401A)

MOTHER GOOSE

J. W. ELLIOTT

LISTEN   SING

Lit-tle Bo-peep has lost her sheep, And

can't tell where to find them;

LISTEN

Leave them a-lone and they'll come home,

SING

Wag-ging their tails be-hind them.

28

Away in a Manger

(2002A)

Gently

SING

1. A - way in a man - ger, No crib for a bed,
2. The cat - tle are low - ing, The poor ba - by wakes,

LISTEN

The lit - tle Lord Je - sus Laid down his sweet head;
But lit - tle Lord Je - sus, No cry - ing He makes;

SING

The stars in the sky___ Look'd down where He lay,
I love Thee, Lord Je - sus, Look down from the sky,

LISTEN

The Lit - tle Lord Je - sus, a - sleep on the hay.
And stay by my cra - dle 'Till morn - ing is nigh.

Note : May be sung in two parts.

29

This Is Mother's Knives and Forks
(2201A)

TRADITIONAL FINGERPLAY SONG
Accompaniment by I.W.

This is moth-er's knives and forks, And this is moth-er's ta - ble;

Here is sis-ter's look-ing-glass, And this is the ba - by's cra - dle.

Fingerplay :-

First phrase: Put back of hands together with fingers extended and interlaced, like stacked knives and forks.

Second phrase: Without separating, turn hands over so knuckles are up, forming "mother's table."

Third phrase: Raise the two pointer fingers to make "sister's looking glass" above the table.

Last phrase: Similarly, raise the two little fingers to add the other end of "baby's cradle" and rock from the wrists.

High, Betty Martin
(2201A) NEW ENGLAND FOLK SONG

Lightly

LISTEN   SING

High, Bet-ty Mar-tin, tip-toe, tip-toe, High, Bet-ty Mar-tin, tip-toe fine;
Nev-er found a boy to suit her fan-cy, Nev-er found a boy to please her mind.

LISTEN   SING

Tra-la-la-la-la-la-la-la, Tra-la-la-la-la-la-la-la, Tra-la-la-la-la-la-la-la, tip-toe fine.

The Zoo
(401A)

ARTHUR HENRY
Not too slowly

ALYS E. BENTLEY
Acc. by I.W.

I like to watch the tall gi-raffe, The seal and kan-ga-roo,

And all the friend-ly an-i-mals That gath-er at the Zoo,

I like to hear the bears go "Woof" And see the mon-keys play.

When I can trav-el by my-self, I'm go-ing there to stay.

Sky Music

VICTOR N. PIERPONT

(301A) NORFOLK CHIMES
Acc. by I.W.

Steadily, smoothly   SING   LISTEN

1. We are the chimes that weave the hours,
2. Out of the sky we bring a tune,
   Sol mi do sol sol re sol mi

SING   LISTEN

Mak- ing them sweet as chains of flowers.
Ev- er the same from June to June.
Sol mi do sol sol re mi do.

See how many of your entire group can play the easy piano accompaniment for "Sky Music" or "Diddle, Diddle Dumpling."

KATE FORMAN

(301A) *Swing Song*

Step-bend step-bend   walk walk step-bend Step-bend step-bend walk walk step-bend
Swing, swing low and high, Swing, swing low and high,
Sol mi re do sol Sol mi re do sol

Walk walk walk walk walk walk walk walk Step-bend step-bend   step 2-3-4.
Catch a lit- tle wil- low leaf As you pass by.
Do do re mi fa mi re re sol sol do.

Step the notes of "Swing Song." Can you feel the *two* pulses of the half-notes? First a forward *step* (count one) and then a *bend* of the knee (count two) with your weight on the same foot. Take only one forward step for each note.

Did You Ever See a Lassie?

ENGLISH SINGING GAME

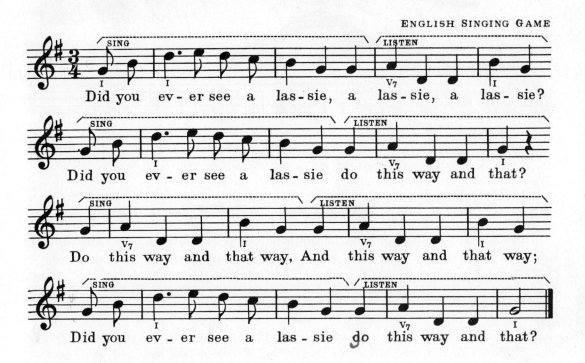

SING
Did you ev-er see a las-sie, a las-sie, a las-sie?
I I LISTEN V7 I

SING
Did you ev-er see a las-sie do this way and that?
I LISTEN V7 I

SING
Do this way and that way, And this way and that way;
V7 I LISTEN V7 I

SING
Did you ev-er see a las-sie do this way and that?
I LISTEN V7 I

The Windmill

GERMAN AIR

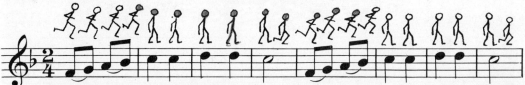

Run run run run walk walk walk walk step-bend. Run run run run walk walk walk walk step-bend.

Look on yon-der grass-y hill Stands the ev-er turn-ing mill;
Do re mi fa sol we climb the hill Do re mi fa sol we're up there still.

Walk walk walk walk walk walk step-bend. Walk walk walk walk walk walk step-bend.

How the wind with whis-tling sound Moves the long arms 'round and 'round.
Then come down-ward in a row, *Fa fa mi mi re re do.*

From *The Modern Music Series*, by permission of Silver Burdett Co., New York, owners of the copyright.

Can you feel the running notes of the "Windmill Song"? Can you tell when the notes *walk?* Try stepping with the notes, like the little figures above the notes.

Hush, My Babe

Isaac Watts

With gentle movement

J. J. Rousseau

Fine (End)

Hush, my babe, lie still and slum-ber, Ho-ly an-gels guard thy bed,
D. C. When from heav-en He de-scend-ed And be-came a child like thee.
Mi mi re do do re re mi re do Sol sol fa mi mi re do re mi do.

Heav'n-ly bless-ings with-out num-ber, Gen-tly fall-ing on thy head.
Mi mi re do do re re mi re do Sol sol fa mi mi re do re mi do.

D. C.

How much bet-ter thou'rt at-tend-ed Than the Son of God could be,
Mi mi fa sol sol la la sol fa mi Mi mi fa sol sol la la sol

My Pony

G. A. Grant-Schaefer

G. A. Grant-Schaefer

SING

1. I have a lit-tle po-ny Jack, with coat of shin-ing brown, And
2. And when I've gal-loped all a-bout and spent a hap-py day, I

LISTEN

all day long I gal-lop and gal-lop and gal-lop a-round the town.
ride him home a-gain to his sta-ble and feed him on nice sweet hay.

34

Song of the Cricket

G. A. GRANT-SCHAEFER

Very smoothly

Oh, hear the crick - et sing - ing his song so bright;

Stars shine a - bove us, now comes the night.

Oh, keep on sing - ing till night is gone;

Sing on till morn - ing comes with the dawn.

Hey, Diddle Diddle

MOTHER GOOSE

J. W. ELLIOTT

Quickly, in fun

Hey, did-dle did-dle, the cat and the fid-dle! The cow jumped o-ver the moon; The lit-tle dog laugh'd to see such sport, And the dish ran aft-er the spoon.

Twinkle, Twinkle, Little Star

J. W. ELLIOTT

Very lightly

1. Twin-kle, twin-kle, lit-tle star, How I won-der what you
2. When the blaz-ing sun is gone, When he noth-ing shines up-
3. As your bright and ti-ny spark, Lights the trav-'ler in the

are! Up a-bove the world so high, Like a dia-mond in the sky.
on, Then you show your lit-tle light, Twin-kle, twin-kle, all the night.
dark, Tho' I know not what you are, Twin-kle, twin-kle, lit-tle star.

36

The Gardener

FRENCH FOLK SONG

With an easy swing

SING

1. This is how we dig the ground
   Do mi sol do sol mi do

LISTEN / SING

In our pret-ty gar-den bed. This is how we
ti do re re do re mi do mi sol do

LISTEN

dig the ground In the ear-ly morn - ing.
sol mi do ti do re fa mi re do.

2. Smooth the ground. 4. Hoe the weeds.
3. Sow the seed.   5. Pick the corn.

Bow-wow-wow

(301A)

MOTHER GOOSE

Quickly

SING

Bow - wow - wow!
Do do do

LISTEN

Whose dog art thou?
do re mi fa sol

SING

Lit - tle Tom - my Tuck - er's dog, Bow-wow-wow!
sol la ti do ti la sol fa mi re do.

37

See-Saw, Margery Daw
(401A)

MOTHER GOOSE   J. W. ELLIOTT

With strong rhythm

See - saw, Mar - ger - y Daw,

Jack shall have a new mas - ter;

He shall have but a pen - ny a day,

Be - cause he won't work an - y fast - er.

The Muffin Man
(201B)

SINGING GAME

With gay movement

1. O do you know the muf-fin man, The muf-fin man, the
2. O yes, I know the muf-fin man, The muf-fin man, the

muf-fin man, O do you know the muf-fin man, That lives in Dru-ry Lane?
muf-fin man, O yes, I know the muf-fin man, That lives in Dru-ry Lane.

"The Muffin Man" is a singing game of choosing and counting, in which
a player skips in time to the music while another child is seated; the player
sings a stanza which is answered by the other. The two then join hands and
dance around the circle singing, "Two of us know," etc.

Jack-in-the-Pulpit

C. SMITH   J. L. G.

Animato (with spirit)

SING

Jack in the pul - pit
Do   re   mi   sol   sol

LISTEN

preach - es   to - day,
do   re   mi   la

SING   LISTEN

Un - der the green leaf just o - ver the way.
sol   la   ti   do   sol   fa   mi   re   mi   do

A-Hunting We Will Go

(401A)

SINGING GAME

Oh, a - hunt-ing we will go, a - hunt-ing we will go, We'll

catch a fox and put him in a box, And nev - er let him go.

HOW TO PLAY THE GAME

The children form into sets of twelve, with two parallel lines of six in each, facing each other.

Measures 1 to 4: The head partners in each set join hands and slide down toward the end of the set, while the children sing and clap the rhythm.

Measures 5 to 8: The same partners slide back to the head of the set, while the children in the line sing and clap.

Chorus: (All sing "tra-la-la-la-la-la" to the melody.)

The head partners separate and lead their respective lines with skipping step down outside lines to end of set. They join hands overhead, and remain at end of set while other couples skip through. A new couple is at the head as game is repeated. Play the game until the first couple heads the line again.

The Music Box

(101B)

FREDERICK WINTHROP · OLD FRENCH AIR, "AMARYLLIS"

Walk walk walk walk walk walk step-bend walk walk walk walk run run run run walk walk

1. Now the mu-sic box will play, Grand-ma took the key and wound it.
2. Grand-ma says 'twas made in France, That is where she says she found it.

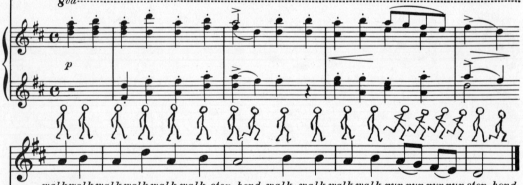

walk walk walk walk walk walk step-bend walk walk walk walk run run run run step-bend.

All its tunes are bright and gay, Though they most-ly sound the same.
Hear this queer old-fash-ioned dance; "Am-a-ryl-lis" is its name.

WHAT DOES IT SAY?

We are told that music is a language which is understood by everyone. Music always has something to say—something of peace, or joy, or longing, or worship, or fun, or story. See if you can discover its message, its mood, its feeling. If you can, you will enjoy it much more.

Whenever we sing or play, we must find out *what* it is that we are to express and *how* we are to say it.

The Nightingale
(203A)

KATE FORMAN

DR. GARRETT
Acc. by I.W.

Legato (well connected)

1. When the rob - in's gone to sleep,
2. Is   the night-in-gale a bird,

When the moon is   bright,   Then a love-ly bird I hear,
Far a-way from sight,   Or a love-ly an-gel dream,

Sing-ing in   the night,   Sing-ing in   the night.
Sing-ing in   the night,   Sing-ing in   the night?

41

The Little Shoemaker
(402A)

ALICE C. D. RILEY

JESSIE L. GAYNOR

Allegretto (somewhat quick)

SING

1. There's a lit-tle wee man in a
2. He puts his nee-dle

LISTEN

SING

lit-tle wee house, Lives o-ver the way you see, And he
in and out, His thread flies to and fro, With his

LISTEN

sits at the win-dow and sews all day, Mak-ing shoes for you and me.
ti-ny awl he bores the holes, Hear the ham-mer's bus-y blow.

Accompaniment staccato

42

A-rap a-tap tap,   A-rap a-tap tap, Hear the ham-mer's tit-tat - tee.

A-rap a-tap tap,   A-rap a-tap tap, Mak-ing shoes for you and me.

Susy, Little Susy
(101A)

ENGELBERT HUMPERDINCK
From "Hänsel and Gretel"

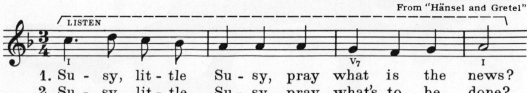

1. Su - sy, lit - tle Su - sy, pray what is the news?
2. Su - sy, lit - tle Su - sy, pray what's to be done?

Sol la sol fa mi mi mi re do re mi

The geese are run - ning bare - foot be - cause they've no shoes!
Who'll give me milk and sug - ar, for bread I have none?

do sol la sol fa mi fa mi re do re do

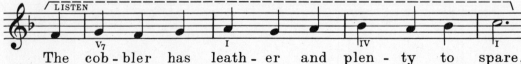

The cob - bler has leath - er and plen - ty to spare,
I'll sell my soft bed and go sleep in the hay,

do re do re mi re mi fa mi fa sol

Why ___ can't he make the poor geese a new pair?
Su - sy, lit - tle Su - sy, some pen - nies, I pray.

sol la sol fa mi fa mi re do re do

Can you feel how fast the horses are galloping in this music? Perhaps you can imagine a story about it.

The Wild Horseman

SCHUMANN

Captain Jinks

When Cap-tain Jinks comes home at night He claps his hands with

all his might. Sa-lute your part-ner, smile so bright, For that's the style in the

ar - my.   Join your hands and for-ward all; Back-ward all, back-ward all;

Join your hands and for-ward all, For that's the style in the   ar - my.

SECOND PART; SAME TUNE

4. When Captain Jinks comes home at night,
   The gentleman passes to the right.

5. Swing your partner so polite,
   For that's the style in the army.

6. Promenade all around the hall,
   Around the hall, around the hall;
   Promenade all around the hall,
   For that's the style in the army

Formation: Couples in a single circle, facing in.
Action: (1) Clap hands. (2) All bow to partners. (3) Join hands in com-
plete circle and march to the center and back twice. (4) Gentleman crosses
in front of his own partner and takes partner of man on his right. (5) Swing
lady once around and keep her for new partner. (6) Promenade counter-
clockwise until song is finished. Then start over.

Dance Song
(102A)

M. Louise Baum

DANISH FOLK SONG
Acc. by I.W.

Two pulses per measure

LISTEN

1. The fid-dles are tun-ing 'tis time for the dance,
2. We swing in a cir-cle and bal-ance a-gain,
3. For-get-ting to-mor-row and trou-bles that come,

SING

Tak-ing hands a-round we go sway-ing,
Ev-'ry heel and toe step-ping light-ly,
But an hour we take for our pleas-ure,

LISTEN

We're croon-ing to the tun-ing in the moon-light,
We're croon-ing to the tun-ing in the moon-light,
We're croon-ing to the tun-ing in the moon-light,

SING

In time and in rhyme with the play-ing.
While fid-dles are play-ing so bright-ly.
And dance to the mu-si-cal meas-ure.

Dancing in May

ELIZABETH NOXON   CARL WILHELM

1. Let us be danc-ing, hap-pi-ly pranc-ing, Ev-'ry-thing's
2. Snow-white and mer-ry, blooms of the cher-ry, Wav-ing a-
3. Lis-ten, O lis-ten! fair-y wings glis-ten, There where the

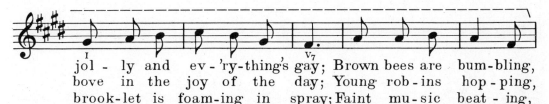

jol-ly and ev-'ry-thing's gay; Brown bees are bum-bling,
bove in the joy of the day; Young rob-ins hop-ping,
brook-let is foam-ing in spray; Faint mu-sic beat-ing,

lamb-kins are tum-bling; Ev-'ry-thing frol-ic-some danc-es in May.
lit-tle wings flop-ping; Ev-'ry-thing beau-ti-ful danc-es in May.
fair-y forms meet-ing; Ev-'ry-thing won-der-ful danc-es in May.

MUSIC ABOUT THE OUT-OF-DOORS

Here are the first themes of two little tone pictures of the out-of-doors, written for the piano but often played by other instruments.

"Spring Song" is by the German composer, Mendelssohn.

"To a Wild Rose" is one of six short pieces called "Woodland Sketches." It was composed in 1896 by the famous American composer, Edward Mac-Dowell. This music is as simple and bright as the flower we love to see along the roadside. Perhaps some of you who have studied piano can play the whole piece at the piano.

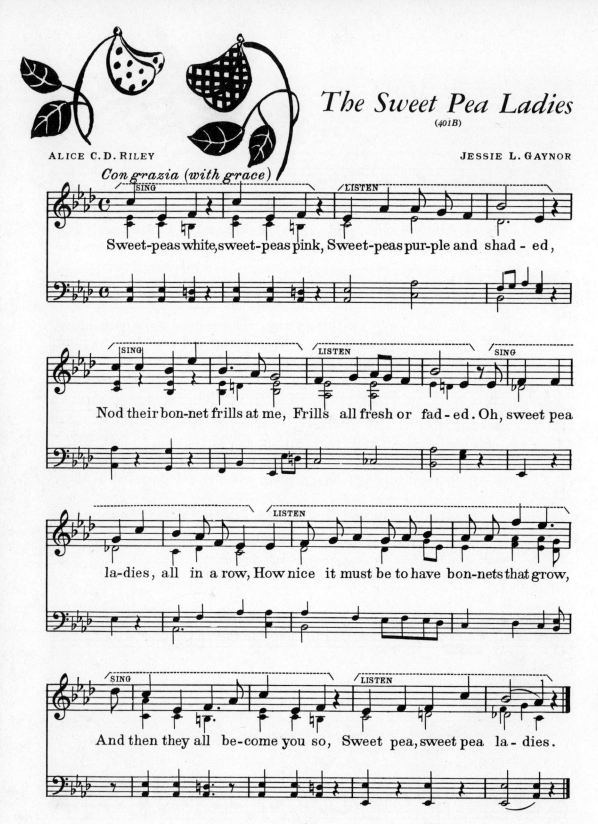

The Sweet Pea Ladies
(401B)

ALICE C. D. RILEY

JESSIE L. GAYNOR

Con grazia (with grace)

SING

LISTEN

Sweet-peas white, sweet-peas pink, Sweet-peas pur-ple and shad - ed,

SING

LISTEN

SING

Nod their bon-net frills at me, Frills all fresh or fad - ed. Oh, sweet pea

LISTEN

la-dies, all in a row, How nice it must be to have bon-nets that grow,

SING

LISTEN

And then they all be-come you so, Sweet pea, sweet pea la - dies.

48

Soldier Boys
(401B)

Rose Craighill

Alys E. Bentley

CLASS MARK TIME   **MARCH AND SING**

For-ward march! Boys, Brave and true and strong,

Marcato (accented)

Read-y! Stead-y! Bear-ing the flag a-long. Tr-r-um, Tr-r-um, Tr-um, Tr-um, Tr-um

MARK TIME

Sol-dier boys, Sol-dier boys, Sing-ing a sol-dier song.

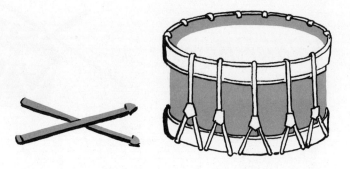

RHYTHM IS THE HEARTBEAT OF MUSIC

Can you feel it going?

Much of all our music has delightful movement in it—movements like those of swaying trees, rustling corn, birds in flight, cantering horses, or the skip-skip-skip of our feet. It is the movement of music that gives it pulsing life and vigor.

If we *feel* that movement, the music makes us run quickly or step bravely with a never-give-up kind of stubborn determination; or it makes us go gently, thoughtfully; or sometimes it makes us skim rapidly with light steps, or whirl and whirl until we are breathing fast; or again it helps us to glide gracefully with a partner, or pull together when we need the strength of a mighty giant.

But this kind of joy with music must be *earned*. We discover it only by *moving ourselves with the music*. We must listen to the way it goes, then we must move with it freely, generously, so we really *feel the movement*. When we have done so a good many times we can imagine ourselves moving with the music as we listen, or as we sing or play. Once we have discovered this joy in music, it is ours forever.

Does this music tell you how to march?

March of the Little Lead Soldiers PIERNÉ

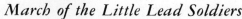

Marche Militaire SCHUBERT

Good Morning!

KATE FORMAN   ARTHUR EDWARD JOHNSTONE

LISTEN   SING   LISTEN   SING

1. "Good morn-ing!" "Good morn-ing!" "Good morn-ing!" "Good morn-ing!"
2. "Good morn-ing!" "Good morn-ing!" "Good morn-ing!" "Good morn-ing!"
3. "Good morn-ing!" "Good morn-ing!" "Good morn-ing!" "Good morn-ing!"

LISTEN

"I'm ver - y glad to see you; I hope you've come to stay."
"And now we must be go - ing, We've stayed al - most an hour!"
"We hope you'll come to our house, And make a vis - it too."

SING   LISTEN   SING

"Good morn-ing!" "Good morn-ing!" "Good morn-ing!" "Good morn-ing!"
"Good morn-ing!" "Good morn-ing!" "Good morn-ing!" "Good morn-ing!"
"Good morn-ing!" "Good morn-ing!" "Good morn-ing!" "Good morn-ing!"

LISTEN

"We've brought a - long our play-things for a long, long play."
"Oh, if you must be go - ing you must take a flow'r!"
"And if you'll ask us now, we'll all go home with you."

A Merry Song

(103A)

MAY SARSON   MAY SARSON

SING

1. Mer-ri-ly turns the spin-ner's wheel:
2. Mer-ri-ly turns the mil-ler's sail:

LISTEN

What shall we make to - day?
What does he grind to - day?

SING   LISTEN

Some dain-ty stuff for a   fine new gown For Jen-ny to wear when she
Some wheat and bar-ley that we can bake For John-ny a nice lit-tle

SING   LISTEN

goes to town. Hey, ho, Where shall we go? Jen-ny's the nic-est girl I know!
sug-ar cake. Hey, ho, Who told you so? John-ny's the nic-est boy I know!

52

There Stands a Little Man

(101A)

ENGELBERT HUMPERDINCK
From "Hänsel and Gretel"

1. There stands a lit-tle man in the wood a-lone,
2. His hair is all of gold and his cheeks are red,
   Sol do re mi fa sol la fa mi re do

He wears a lit-tle man-tle of vel-vet brown.
He wears a lit-tle black cap up-on his head.
Sol do re mi fa sol la fa mi re do

Say, who can the man-kin be, Stand-ing there be-neath the tree,
Say, who can the man-kin be, Stand-ing there so si-lent-ly,
Sol fa mi sol fa mi re Sol fa mi sol fa mi re

With the lit-tle man-tle of vel-vet brown?
With the lit-tle black cap up-on his head?*
do re mi fa sol do la fa mi re do

* A Toadstool

Wing Foo

ROSE CRAIGHILL   HARVEY WORTHINGTON LOOMIS

Rather fast, with marked rhythm

Wing Foo, Chi-na boy, up-side down; That is how he looks to me.

When I'm ly-ing in bed at night, Play-ing in the sun is he.

The Dairy Maids

JAMES SLOCUM

OLD ENGLISH TUNE

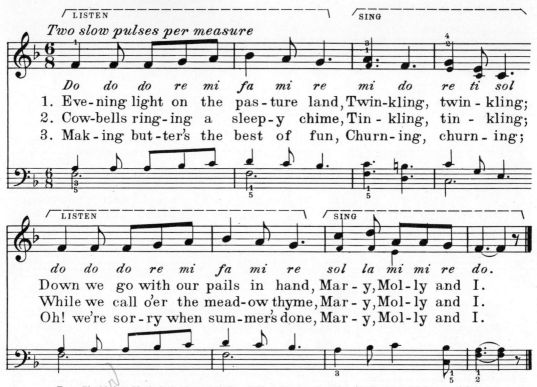

Two slow pulses per measure

LISTEN   SING

Do do do re mi fa mi re mi do re ti sol

1. Eve-ning light on the pas-ture land, Twin-kling, twin-kling;
2. Cow-bells ring-ing a sleep-y chime, Tin-kling, tin-kling;
3. Mak-ing but-ter's the best of fun, Churn-ing, churn-ing;

LISTEN   SING

do do do re mi fa mi re sol la mi mi re do.

Down we go with our pails in hand, Mar-y, Mol-ly and I.
While we call o'er the mead-ow thyme, Mar-y, Mol-ly and I.
Oh! we're sor-ry when sum-mer's done, Mar-y, Mol-ly and I.

From *The Modern Music Series*, by permission of Silver Burdett Co., New York, owners of the copyright.

Dame, Get Up

(101B)

MAY SARSON
(Stanzas 2 & 3)

OLD ENGLISH SONG

SING   LISTEN

1. Dame, get up   and bake your pies, bake your pies, bake your pies,
2. Dame, what makes them taste so nice, taste so nice, taste so nice,
3. I   filled them all with sug-ar spice, sug-ar spice, sug-ar spice,

SING   LISTEN

Dame, get up   and bake your pies, on Christ-mas day in the morn-ing.
Dame, what makes them taste so nice, on Christ-mas day in the morn-ing?
I   filled them all with sug-ar spice, on Christ-mas day in the morn-ing.

54

The Brownies

ALICE C. D. RILEY

JESSIE L. GAYNOR

Leggiero (lightly)

1. Hist! Hist! be still, on tip-toe now ad-vance,
2. Oh we're as light as this-tle-down or dew,

We've come to have a mer-ry brown-ies dance;
We're brown-ies of the brown-ie band so true,

We will form our cir-cle here, Step-ping light-ly for we fear
And we dance the live-long night, Van-ish with the morn-ing light,

We may wak-en all the sleep-ing world per-chance.
Hid-ing safe from mor-tal vi-sion and from you.

We will form our cir-cle here, Step-ping light-ly for we fear
And we dance the live-long night, Van-ish with the morn-ing light,

We may wak-en all the sleep-ing world per-chance.
Hid-ing safe from mor-tal vi-sion and from you.

God's Gifts

(402B)

CHARLES ELLERTON

Attributed to
W. A. MOZART

LISTEN   SING

1. There's a sun for the morn-ing, And a moon for the night;
2. Light and warmth, joy and beau-ty Come from God high a-bove,

LISTEN   SING

When the moon hides her face, Still the stars twin-kle bright.
And he gives these good gifts From a heart full of love.

Pop Goes the Weasel
(2201B)

TRADITIONAL

AMERICAN SINGING GAME

Vivace (lively)

All a-round the chick-en coop The mon-key chased the wea-sel,

The mon-key thought 'twas all in fun, Pop! goes the wea-sel.

A pen-ny for a spool of thread, A pen-ny for a nee-dle,

That's the way the mon-ey goes, Pop! goes the wea-sel.

Naming the Trees

REBECCA B. FORESMAN

GERMAN FOLK SONG

Allegro (quick)

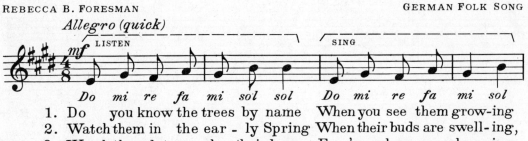

LISTEN — SING

Do mi re fa mi sol sol Do mi re fa mi sol

1. Do you know the trees by name When you see them grow-ing
2. Watch them in the ear-ly Spring When their buds are swell-ing,
3. Watch them lat-er when their leaves Ev-'ry-where are show-ing,

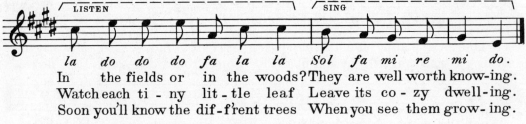

LISTEN — SING

la do do do fa la la Sol fa mi re mi do.

In the fields or in the woods? They are well worth know-ing.
Watch each ti-ny lit-tle leaf Leave its co-zy dwell-ing.
Soon you'll know the dif-f'rent trees When you see them grow-ing.

A True Story

(401B)

Acc. by I.W

LISTEN

SING

Allegro (quick)

1. Two lit-tle chip-munks sat up-on a rail, sat up-on a rail,
2. One lit-tle chip-munk, sit-ting all a-lone, sit-ting all a-lone,

LISTEN

SING

Each had a fluffed out feath-er for a tail, feath-er for a tail.
Picked up a nut and found it was a bone, found it was a bone.

LISTEN

One jumped down and ran to town With a
This I know is all just so, For I

SING

let-ter for the mail, let-ter for the mail.
heard it on the phone, heard it on the phone.

★ This measure, piano octave higher, voice like previous measure.

Company

(402B)

ARTHUR EDWARD JOHNSTONE
Acc. by I.W.

Two pulses per measure

SING
LISTEN

1. Com - pa - ny's come to spend the day, Girls and boys and
2. Aft - er the games we all will sing, Girls and boys and
3. Then in the eve - ning 'round the grate, Girls and boys and

SING

old - er peo-ple; Think of the games we all may play!
old - er peo-ple; Mer - ri - est mu - sic then will ring;
old - er peo-ple; Won - der - ful sto - ries we'll re - late;

LISTEN

Hop - scotch, leap - frog, hi - spy too,
Gay songs, sad songs, soft and low,
Old ones, new ones, grave or bright,

Base - ball, foot - ball, these are just a few.
Folk songs, school songs, ev - 'ry one must know.
Short ones, long ones, then we'll say "Good Night!"

The Brooklet
(402A)

From the Russian

RUSSIAN FOLK SONG
Acc. by I.W.

Run run run run walk walk walk walk step-bend   Run run run run walk walk walk walk step-bend

1. Hap-py lit-tle brook-let, how you play Un-der-neath the wil low all the day,
2. Ev-'ry day I won-der where you go, When you leave the hill and drop be-low;
3. Still, I al-ways find you glad and gay, Un-der-neath the wil low where you play;

Step-change-step walk walk walk walk step-bend Step-change-step walk walk walk walk step-bend.

Run - ning 'round in pools of light, Leap - ing o - ver peb-bles bright.
Dark and deep your wa-ters fall; All the night you call and call.
Ev - 'ry morn-ing fresh and free, There you smile and run to me.

Advice
(402A)

MAY SARSON

MAY SARSON

In a sprightly manner

LISTEN   SING   LISTEN

1. Jen-ni-fer-do, Jen-ni-fer-dine, Comb your locks as I do mine. Then you'll
2. Jen-ni-fer-do, Jen-ni-fer-dine, Wear your hat as I do mine. Then you'll
3. Jen-ni-fer-do, Jen-ni-fer-dine, Give your flow'rs as I give mine. If you

SING

look so pret-ty and neat And be quite the fair-est in the street.
look so mer-ry and gay And you'll steal a hun-dred hearts a-way.
lock them all a-way You will find them with-ered one fine day.

59

Little Friends

Arr. and translated
From the Chinese by Bliss Wiant

CHINESE FOLK MELODY
Arr. by Bliss Wiant

Rather quickly

Lit - tle friends, All are lit - tle friends; We are all such

good lit - tle friends! Old - er play-mates, young - er play-mates,

lit - tle play-mates too, Come! let's all join hands to-geth - er

as we like to do. Step by step we for - ward go;

On and on up-on our path with light a-glow: Lit-tle friends.

Polka Gay

(101B)

MAY SARSON   MAY SARSON

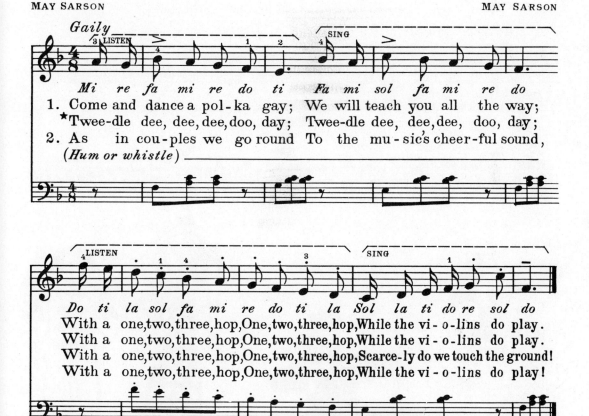

Mi re fa mi re do ti Fa mi sol fa mi re do

1. Come and dance a pol-ka gay; We will teach you all the way;
*Twee-dle dee, dee, dee, doo, day; Twee-dle dee, dee, dee, doo, day;
2. As in cou-ples we go round To the mu-sic's cheer-ful sound,
(*Hum or whistle*)

Do ti la sol fa mi re do ti la Sol la ti do re sol do

With a one, two, three, hop, One, two, three, hop, While the vi-o-lins do play.
With a one, two, three, hop, One, two, three, hop, While the vi-o-lins do play.
With a one, two, three, hop, One, two, three, hop, Scarce-ly do we touch the ground!
With a one, two, three, hop, One, two, three, hop, While the vi-o-lins do play!

★ In imitation of violins, clapping lightly for the rhythm of the feet.

61

NUTCRACKER SUITE

Some of our most delightful music was written to help tell a story. The Russian composer, Tschaikowsky, wrote this orchestral music for the ballet, in which very wonderful dancers, by their acting and dancing, tell the story of the silver nutcracker.

This is the story of a thrilling dream which a little girl named Marie had after the excitement of her Christmas party. When she came downstairs to have one more look at her beautiful gifts, Marie was frightened by a great big mouse. But she was rescued by her new silver nutcracker, which turned into a shiny prince and bravely fought this king of the mice. He then took her to Jam Mountain, where the Sugar-Plum fairy had a royal party in their honor. Here were Marie's dolls and toys, very much alive and beautifully costumed, ready to entertain her.

First to dance was the Sugar-Plum fairy herself, then the Russian dolls, the Arabian dolls, the Chinese dolls, and the three little toy flutists. Finally Princess Marie, Prince Nutcracker, and everyone joined in the "Waltz of the Flowers."

The titles of the eight pieces which make up this suite will help you to know what part of the story this music is describing. The "Miniature Overture" seems to suggest the gay spirit of the Christmas party.

Allegro giusto

The "March" is for all the toy soldiers, or possibly the happy guests entering in a grand procession into the ballroom.

For the "Dance of the Sugar-Plum Fairy" we hear a very lovely and unusual instrument of the orchestra called the celesta, bell-like in sound and played by keys like a piano.

"The Dance of the Toy Flutes" simply sparkles! Can you hear three flutes?

The "Waltz of the Flowers" begins with a festive introduction in which we hear the shimmery harp. Then a very lovely melody by the French horns starts the graceful waltz.

dolce cantabile

Morning Song

JOHN FERGUSON

(102A) OLD ENGLISH
Acc. by I.W.

LISTEN · SING

Two definite pulses per measure

1. The sun is ris-ing out of bed, And in the East the sky is red;
2. The light is clear on hill and lea, The birds are loud in ev-'ry tree;
3. Where 'neath the share the fur-rows gleam, We'll see the plough-man drive his team,

Then up and wake each sleep-y head, So ear-ly in the morn-ing.
Then haste and rise and come with me, So ear-ly in the morn-ing.
Or wan-der down be-side the stream, So ear-ly in the morn-ing.

'Tis shame to dream the hours a-way, When all the world is bright with day,
With pleas-ant sights and sounds to spare, With hearts a-lert and free from care,
And where the wa-ter's fresh and cool, We'll watch the trout with-in the pool;

poco rit.

And Na-ture calls to work or play, So ear-ly in the morn-ing.
We'll out and drink the whole-some air, So ear-ly in the morn-ing.
There's time be-fore we go to school, So ear-ly in the morn-ing.

64

The Tailor and the Mouse

ENGLISH FOLK SONG

1. There was a tai-lor had a mouse, Hi did-dle un-kum fee-dle!
2. The tai-lor tho't the mouse was ill, Hi did-dle un-kum fee-dle!
3. The tai-lor tho't his mouse would die, Hi did-dle un-kum fee-dle!
4. The pie was cut, the mouse ran out, Hi did-dle un-kum fee-dle!
5. The tai-lor found his mouse was dead, Hi did-dle un-kum fee-dle!

They lived to-geth-er in one house, Hi did-dle un-kum fee-dle!
He gave him part of a blue pill. Hi did-dle un-kum fee-dle!
He baked him in an ap-ple pie, Hi did-dle un-kum fee-dle!
The tai-lor fol-lowed him a-bout, Hi did-dle un-kum fee-dle!
So he caught an-oth-er in his stead, Hi did-dle un-kum fee-dle!
Hi did-dle un-kum o-ver the lea, Hi did-dle un-kum fee-dle!

CHORUS

Hi did-dle un-kum tar-um tan-tum Thru the town of Ram-say.

65

Three Little Girls
(103A)

AMERICAN SINGING GAME   Arr. by G. V. N.

LISTEN   SING

1. Three lit-tle girls went slid-ing on the ice, Slid-ing on the ice,

LISTEN   SING

slid-ing on the ice; Three lit-tle girls went slid-ing on the ice, So

CHORUS LISTEN

ear - ly in the month of May. Swing them all a-round as you

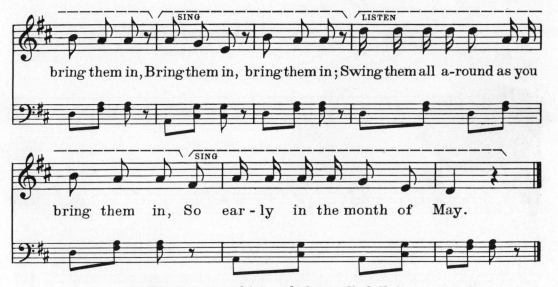

bring them in, Bring them in, bring them in; Swing them all a-round as you

bring them in, So ear-ly in the month of May.

2. The ice was thin and they all fell in,
They all fell in, they all fell in.
The ice was thin and they all fell in
So early in the month of May.

The first eight measures should be played twice before playing the chorus. The above words are sung on the repetition of these measures.

Formation: One large circle, hands joined. One small circle of three dancers (girls) in the center of the large circle, hands joined.

First stanza: Circles slide around in opposite directions.

Second stanza: Reverse directions.

Chorus: The big circle stands in place. The girls in the center skip out to the circle; each chooses a boy; partners join both hands, skip into the center, whirling as they go. The girl leaves her partner there and joins the circle.

The game is started again with the three boys forming the small circle in the center. The word "boys" is now sung in place of "girls" in the first stanza.

Sweet Be Your Rest

(402B)

MAY SARSON

OLD CELTIC LULLABY
Acc. by M.S.

1. The lambs are sleep-ing in the fold; The sun has turned the
2. The stars are peep-ing one by one To watch the sink-ing

hills to gold; The eve-ning will be turn-ing cold, So
of the sun; They dare'nt come out till day is done And

come to moth-er, my dar - ling. Creep in-to your
birds and ba-bies are sleep - ing. Lie safe in your

nest, love; I'll sing you to rest, love.
nest, love; Sweet, sweet be your rest, love!

Dancing Song

AMELIA M. SONTAG

RHENISH FOLK SONG

1. Whirl-ing and whirl-ing in cir-cles so light, Danc-ing and
2. Hand-or-gan's mu-sic's as good as a band, Pave-ment is

skip-ping from morn-ing till night, One, two, three; one, two, three;
smooth where we trip hand in hand. One, two, three; one, two, three;

glide to and fro; One, two, three; one, two, three; sing as we go.
see how we fly; One, two, three; one, two, three; Pol-ly and I.

From *The Modern Music Series*, by permission of Silver Burdett Co., New York, owners of the copyright.

Listen to this song, then clap the rhythm to alternate phrases: *Loud* soft soft: *loud* soft soft.

My Little Owlet
(2201B)

LONGFELLOW'S "HIAWATHA"

AMERICAN INDIAN MELODY

Briskly

E-wa-yea, my lit-tle owl-et; Who is this that lights the

wig-wam? With his great eyes lights the wig-wam, lights the wig-wam?

E-wa-yea, my lit-tle owl-et, Who is this that lights the wig-wam?

The Postilion

KARL G. TAUBERT

LISTEN

1. I'll be a gay pos-til-ion,
2. I'll crack my whip so gai-ly,

SING / LISTEN

With boots and spurs I'll go; I'll drive four dash-ing pon-ies,
And drive my "four-in-hand"; I'll be a for-eign trav-'ler

SING / LISTEN

A gold-en horn I'll blow, I'll be a gay pos-til-ion,
And vis-it ev-'ry land, I'll crack my whip so gai-ly,

SING   LISTEN

With boots and spurs I'll go,   I'll drive four dash-ing pon-ies
And drive my "four-in-hand,"   I'll be a for-eign trav-'ler

SING   LISTEN

A gold-en horn I'll blow. Tra-ra, tra-ra, tra-ra, tra-ra.
And vis-it ev-'ry land. Klick-klack, klick-klack, klick-klack, klick-klack.

Sailor Lads
(103A)

SAILOR CHANTEY
Acc. by I.W.

LISTEN   SING

1. Har-dy sail-or lads are we,   O hey ho!
2. See the bil-lows leap and flow,   O hey ho!
3. Now we set the flap-ping sail,   O hey ho!

LISTEN   SING   1   2

Sail-ing on the might-y sea,   O hey ho!   ho!
Down we sink and up we go,   O hey ho!   ho!
So we chase the fly-ing gale,   O hey ho!   ho!

The Galway Piper
(102A)

TRADITIONAL

IRISH FOLK SONG
Acc. by W. I.

With perky movement

1. Ev-'ry per-son in the na-tion, Or of great or hum-ble sta-tion,
2. When the wed-ding bells are ring-ing, His the breath to lead the sing-ing,
3. When he walks the high-way peal-ing, Round his head the birds come wheeling,

Holds in high-est es-ti-ma-tion, Pip-ing Tim of Gal-way;
Then in jigs the folks go swing-ing, What a splen-did pip-er!
Tim has car-ols worth the steal-ing, Pip-ing Tim of Gal-way.

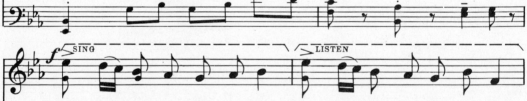

Loud-ly he can play or low, He can move you fast or slow,
He will blow from eve till morn, Count-ing sleep a thing of scorn,
Thrush and lin-net, finch and lark, To each oth-er twit-ter "Hark!"

Touch your hearts or stir your toe, Pip-ing Tim of Gal-way.
Old is he but not out-worn, Know you such a pip-er?
Soon they sing from light till dark, Pip-ings learned in Gal-way.

Fiddle-De-Dee

OLD ENGLISH FOLK SONG

SING ——— LISTEN

1. Fid-dle-de-dee, Fid-dle-de-dee, The fly has mar-ried the
2. Fid-dle-de-dee, Fid-dle-de-dee, The fly has mar-ried the

bum-ble bee. Says the fly, says he, "Will you mar - ry me And
bum-ble bee. Says the bee, says she, "I'll live un-der your wing, And

SING

live with me, sweet bum - ble bee?" Fid-dle-de-dee,
you'll nev-er know I car-ry a sting." Fid-dle-de-dee,

LISTEN

Fid-dle-de-dee, The fly has mar-ried the bum-ble bee.
Fid-dle-de-dee, The fly has mar-ried the bum-ble bee.

The Hummingbird

(103A)

EDWIN STAR BELKNAP

TYROLESE MELODY
Acc. by I.W.

Smoothly, easily

SING ... LISTEN

1. Stay, pret - ty hum - ming - bird, Whis - per your se - cret;
2. Say, pret - ty hum - ming - bird, Are you a fair - y?

SING ... LISTEN

Oh, say pret - ty hum - ming - bird, Have you no song?
Oh, stay pret - ty hum - ming - bird, Show me your wings.

What do you tell to the rose in the dell?
Poised in the air like a flow'r flash - ing fair,

SING ... LISTEN   *rit.*

Oh, say pret - ty hum - ming - bird, Have you no song?
Oh, stay pret - ty hum - ming - bird, Show me your wings.

74

Paw Paw Patch

(2201B)

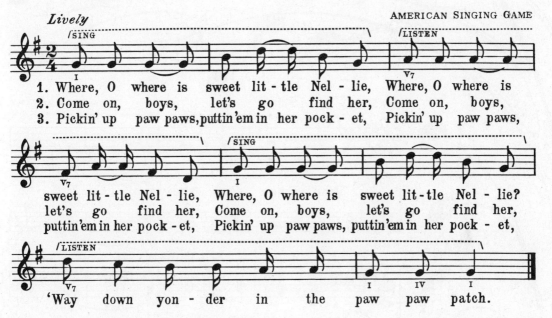

Lively   AMERICAN SINGING GAME

1. Where, O where is sweet lit-tle Nel-lie, Where, O where is
2. Come on, boys, let's go find her, Come on, boys,
3. Pickin' up paw paws, puttin 'em in her pock-et, Pickin' up paw paws,

sweet lit-tle Nel-lie, Where, O where is sweet lit-tle Nel-lie?
let's go find her, Come on, boys, let's go find her,
puttin 'em in her pock-et, Pickin' up paw paws, puttin 'em in her pock-et,

'Way down yon-der in the paw paw patch.

HOW TO PLAY THE GAME:

The boys are in one line, facing their partners in the opposite line. The girls are on the right as the partners face the head of the set.

(1) Sing the first verse to the name of the girl at the head of the line, while she turns to the right and skips down behind the line of girls, then behind the line of boys, and back to her place.

(2) During the second verse, the same girl skips around the set, followed by the line of boys until all are back in place.

(3) Singing the third verse, the first boy in the line joins hands with the first girl, each boy in line takes his partner, and all follow the head couple down the line to the right. At the foot of the line the head couple forms an arch under which the others skip back to their places.

(4) The first verse is sung again to the new girl at the head. Repeat for each girl in turn.

Play the game again for the boys—
"Where, O where is poor little Willie?"

Who Has Seen the Wind?

(103A)

CHRISTINA ROSSETTI   ALYS E. BENTLEY

Who has seen the wind? ____

Nei - ther you nor I ____

But when the trees bow down their heads, The

wind is pass - ing by. ____

A Frog He Would A-Wooing Go

ENGLISH FOLK SONG

LISTEN   SING   LISTEN

1. A Frog he would a-woo-ing go, m-m, m-m, A Frog he would a-
2. He rode right to Miss Mous-ie's den, m-m, m-m, He rode right to Miss
3. Yes, kind Sir Frog, I sit to spin, m-m, m-m, Yes, kind Sir Frog, I
4. He said, my dear I've come to see, m-m, m-m, He said, my dear I've
5. The Frog and Mouse they went to France, m-m, m-m, The Frog and Mouse they

SING

woo-ing go, __ Wheth-er his moth-er would let him or no, m-m, m-m.
Mous-ie's den, Said he __ Miss Mous-ie are you __ with-in? m-m, m-m.
sit to spin, __ Pray, Mis-ter Frog-gie won't you __ walk in? m-m, m-m.
come to see, If you, __ Miss Mous-ie, will mar-ry me? m-m, m-m.
went to France, And that __ is the end of my __ ro-mance, m-m, m-m.

What Music Is This?

(203B)   (2003A)

MAY SARSON

AIR BY CORNER (1649).
Acc. by M.S.

Smoothly, with expressive tone

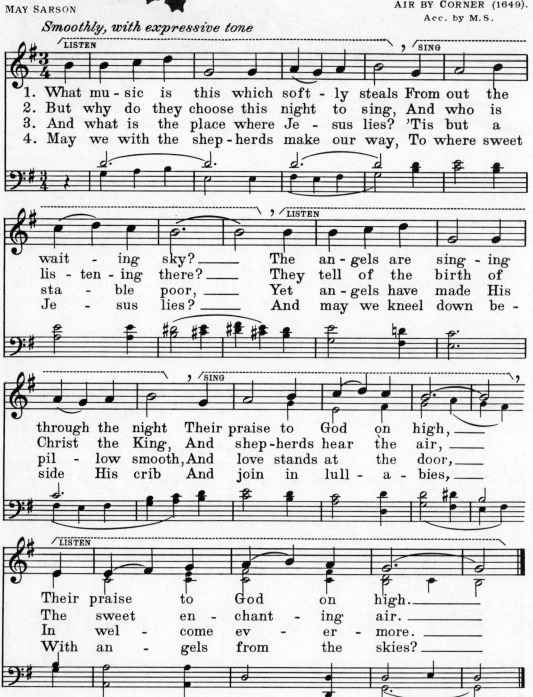

LISTEN

1. What mu-sic is this which soft-ly steals From out the
2. But why do they choose this night to sing, And who is
3. And what is the place where Je-sus lies? 'Tis but a
4. May we with the shep-herds make our way, To where sweet

SING   LISTEN

wait - ing sky?____ The an-gels are sing-ing
lis - ten-ing there?____ They tell of the birth of
sta - ble poor,____ Yet an-gels have made His
Je - sus lies?____ And may we kneel down be-

SING

through the night Their praise to God on high,____
Christ the King, And shep-herds hear the air,____
pil - low smooth, And love stands at the door,____
side His crib And join in lull - a - bies,____

LISTEN

Their praise to God on high.____
The sweet en - chant - ing air.____
In wel - come ev - er - more.____
With an - gels from the skies?____

Lithuanian Lullaby

LITHUANIAN FOLK SONG

1. Sleep my bon - ny blue - eyed lit - tle treas - ure,
2. May the an - gels hov - er ev - er near thee,

Sleep till the ros - y dawn - ing of the day
Lov - ing watch for - ev - er o'er thee keep;

Brings the hap - py hours of pleas - ure; Dream the star - ry
Fair - est vi - sions come to cheer thee; Sleep, my lit - tle

night a - way. Sleep, lit - tle treas - ure.
treas - ure sleep. Sleep, lit - tle treas - ure.

The Little Dustman
(402B)

From "Children's Folk Songs"
By JOHANNES BRAHMS

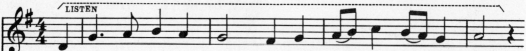

1. The flow'r-lets all sleep sound-ly Be-neath the moon's bright ray;
2. Now see the lit-tle dust-man At the win-dow shows his head,
3. And ere the lit-tle dust-man Is man-y steps a-way,

Quietly

They nod their heads to-geth-er, And dream the night a-way;
And looks for all good chil-dren, Who ought to be in bed,
Thy pret-ty eyes, my dar-ling, Close fast un-til next day;

The bud-ding trees wave to and fro, And mur-mur soft and low.
And as each wea-ry pet he spies Throws dust in-to its eyes.
But they shall ope at morn-ing's light And greet the sun-shine bright.

Sleep on,   sleep   on, sleep on, my lit-tle one.

TWO FAVORITE WALTZES

All of us enjoy the waltz because of its graceful sweep and its buoyant movement. Sometimes it dances dreamily, with a gentle one-two-three, and sometimes it is spirited and fast of movement so we feel only one lilting pulse per measure.

The first theme of two waltzes, different in character, but universally loved:

Waltz in A Flat   BRAHMS

dolce.

Blue Danube Waltz   JOHANN STRAUSS

My Banjo

ITALIAN MELODY

With buoyant movement

SING   LISTEN

1. Tra la la la la, My ban-jo is say-ing, Tra la la la
2. Tra la la la la, The danc-ers are sway-ing, Tra la la la

SING

la. To sound of my play-ing, Tra la la la la, Old friends are the
la. To sound of my play-ing, Tra la la la la, Old friends are the

LISTEN   *Fine.*   SING

dear-est. Come, my ban-jo, we'll sing to them all. Tra la la la la la
dear-est. Come, my ban-jo, we'll sing to them all. Tra la la la la la

Fine.

82

LISTEN *rit.* *D.C.*

la   la   la   la,   Tra la la la   la   la   la   la   la   la la la la la.

rit. *D.C.*

Child's Evensong

JOHN STAINER
Arr. by I.W.

SING   LISTEN

1. From the heav'n a - bove us   'Mid   the an - gels   mild,
2. Boun-teous - ly   He gives us   Food   and rai - ment   still,

SING   LISTEN

Looks a   lov - ing Fa - ther   Down on   ev - 'ry   child.
Gra - cious - ly   He keeps us   From each threat-'ning   ill.

SING   LISTEN

Ten - der - ly   He   lis - tens   When He hears us   pray,
Praise the lov - ing   Fa - ther,   Of His good - ness   tell;

SING   LISTEN

Faith - ful - ly   He guides us   On   our earth - ly   way.
He   will not   for - sake us,   He   doth love us   well.

Evening Song
(403B)

AUSTRIAN FOLK SONG

1. Snug in the lit - tle nest, Bird - ie is sleep - ing;
2. Now the last streak of light, O'er the hills dy - ing,

Shad-ows a - cross the west Slow - ly are creep-ing; Cat - tle that
Fades and the dusk of night Round us is ly - ing; Heav - en, so

go to rest, Herd-boys are call - ing; Eve - ning is fall - ing.
sil - ver bright, O'er us is dream-ing; Soft star-light gleam-ing.

Swiss Song
(403B)

Arr. by W. C. E.

1. When the morn-ing beams a-rise, Yo lo le, yo lo la! Bright-en-ing the
2. Tempt-ed by the fra-grant air, Yo lo le, yo lo la! For the fields we

ros - y skies, Yo lo lay, lo la! From the couch we quick-ly spring,
soon pre-pare, Yo lo lay, lo la! Glo - ry gilds the loft-y trees,

I - dle sloth a - way we fling, Yo lo lay lo lay lo la! Yo lo lay
Branch-es quiv-er in the breeze, yo lo la, Yo lo lay lo lay lo la! Yo lo lay

yo lo la, Yo lo lay lo lay lo la! Yo lo lay lo la!

All Through the Night

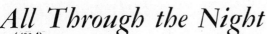

(403A)

OLD WELSH

DAVID OWEN

LISTEN SING

1. {Sleep, my child, and peace at-tend thee, All thru the night.
   {Guard-ian an-gels God will send thee, All thru the night.

2. {While the moon her watch is keep-ing, All thru the night.
   {While the wea-ry world is sleep-ing, All thru the night.

LISTEN

Soft the drow-sy hours are creep-ing, Hill and vale in slum-ber steep-ing,
O'er thy spir-it gen-tly steal-ing, Vi-sion of de-light re-veal-ing,

SING

I my lov-ing vig-il keep-ing, All thru the night.
Breathes a pure and ho-ly feel-ing, All thru the night.

London Bridge

(204B)

ENGLISH SINGING GAME

SING LISTEN

1. Lon-don Bridge is fall-ing down, fall-ing down, fall-ing down,
2. Build it up with i-ron bars, i-ron bars, i-ron bars,

SING LISTEN

Lon-don Bridge is fall-ing down, My Fair La-dy.
Build it up with i-ron bars, My Fair La-dy.

85

Intry, Mintry

Old Rhyme

J. Ramann

Two light pulses per measure

In - try, min - try, cu - trey corn, Ap - ple seed and ap - ple thorn;

Wire, bri - er, lim - ber, lock, Twen - ty geese to make a flock;

Some flew east, some flew west, Some flew o - ver the cuck - oo's nest.

Lightly Row
(303A)

German Folk Tune

1. Light - ly row, light - ly row, O'er the glass - y waves we go,
2. Far a - way, far a - way, Ech - o in the rocks at play
3. Hap - py we, full of glee, Sail - ing on the wav - y sea;

Smooth - ly glide, smooth - ly glide On the si - lent tide.
Call - eth not, call - eth not To this lone - ly spot.
Hap - py we, full of glee, Sail - ing on the sea;

Let the winds and wa - ters be Min - gled with our mel - o - dy;
On - ly with the sea - bird's note Shall our dy - ing mu - sic float;
Lu - na sheds her soft - est light, Stars are spar - kling, twin - kling bright;

Sing and float, sing and float In our lit - tle boat.
Light - ly row, light - ly row, Ech - o's voice is low.
Hap - py we, full of glee, Sail - ing on the sea.

The First Tulip

ELINOR WESTBROOK (203A)

CANON

LISTEN

Allegretto (rather quick)

1. Here, look in the gar-den bed; Some-thing beau-ti-ful is
   small and green; Flame-like, now he is a-

1. Here, look in the gar-den bed;
2. Last night he was small and green;

grow - ing! Bright, shaped like a
glow - ing! This one is the

Some - thing beau - ti - ful is grow - ing!
Flame - like, now he is a - glow - ing!

cup, all red, Tu - lip o - pens to the
first I've seen; Now sweet weath - er is be -

Bright, shaped like a cup, all red,
Sweet tu - lip a gold - en heart

1
sun. 2. Last night he was

Tu - lip o - pens to the sun.

2
gun.

show-ing!

Learn first in unison, then sing as two-part canon

The Frog and the Mouse
(204A)
OLD ENGLISH

With two bounds per measure

LISTEN / SING

1. There was a frog lived in a well, Whip-see did-dle dee dan-dy dee.
   There was a mouse lived in a mill, Whip-see did-dle dee dan-dy dee.
2. He rode till he came to Mouse's Hall, Whip-see did-dle dee dan-dy dee.
   Where he most ten-der-ly did call, Whip-see did-dle dee dan-dy dee.
3. "My un-cle rat is not at home," Whip-see did-dle dee dan-dy dee.
   I dare not for my life come down, Whip-see did-dle dee dan-dy dee.

LISTEN

This frog he would a-woo-ing ride With sword and buck-ler by his side, With a
"Oh Mis-tress Mouse, are you at home? And if you are, oh, pray come down." With a
Then un-cle rat he soon comes home, And who's been here since I've been gone? With a

SING

har-um scar-um did-dle dum da-rum, Whip-see did-dle-dee dan-dy dee.

4. "Here's been a fine young gentleman,
   Who swears he'll have me if he can."
   Then uncle rat gave his consent,
   And made a handsome settlement.

5. Four partridge pies with season made,
   Two potted larks and marmalade,
   Four woodcocks and a venison pie.
   I would that at that feast were I!

88

Hushabye

MAY SARSON

With gentle motion

MAY SARSON
Acc. by I.W.

SING

p

1. Hush - a - bye, hush - a - bye low!
2. Hush - a - bye, hush - a - bye low!
3. Hush - a - bye, hush - a - bye low!

LISTEN

Soft and sweet the sum-mer winds blow; A
Ba - by too shall sail - ing go
When the dawn be - gins to glow,

SING   LISTEN

mf
sil - ver cloud goes sail - ing by A - cross the blue la - goon of sky.
O - ver wa - ters blue and deep, The sil - ver blue la - goon of sleep.
Back to moth - er sails the boat That took her ba - by one a - float.

SING   LISTEN   *poco rit.*

mp
Hush - a - bye, hush - a - bye, Hush - a - bye, bye - low!

Sweet Nightingale
(102A)

ENGLISH FOLK SONG
Acc. by I. W.

SING

1. Pret - ty maid, come a - long! Don't you hear the fond song,
2. Pret - ty Bet - ty don't fail, For I'll car - ry your pail,
3. Prith - ee sit your - self down With me on the ground,

LISTEN

The sweet note of the night - in - gale flow?
Safe - ly home to your cot as we go,
On the bank where the prim - ros - es grow,

SING

Don't you hear the fond tale of the sweet night - in - gale,
You shall hear the fond tale of the sweet night - in - gale,
You shall hear the fond tale of the sweet night - in - gale,

90

As she sings in the valley below? _____
As she sings in the valley below. _____
As she sings in the valley below. _____

_____ As she sings in the valley below?
_____ As she sings in the valley below.
_____ As she sings in the valley below.

"Melody in F," by Rubinstein, is like someone singing a lovely song. Listen for the return of the familiar melody after the different tune of the middle section.

Melody in F   RUBINSTEIN

Moderato ———————————————————————   *rit.*

Vesper Hymn

THOMAS MOORE

RUSSIAN MELODY
Arr. by I.W.

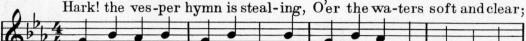

Hark! the ves-per hymn is steal-ing, O'er the wa-ters soft and clear;

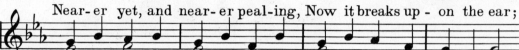

Ding! Dong! Ding! Dong! Ding! Dong! Ding! Dong!

Near-er yet, and near-er peal-ing, Now it breaks up-on the ear;

Ding! Dong! Ding! Dong! Ding! Dong! Ding! Dong!

*Ju-bi-la-te! Ju-bi-la-te! Ju-bi-la-te! A-men.

Far-ther now, now far-ther steal-ing, Soft it fades up-on the ear.

*Latin for "Be joyful!" Pronounce: You-be-lah-tay.

Fairest Lord Jesus

(304A)

ANON. (German)

CRUSADERS' HYMN
Arr. by I.W.

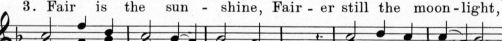

1. Fair-est Lord Je-sus, Rul-er of all na-ture,
2. Fair are the mead-ows, Fair-er still the wood-lands,
3. Fair is the sun-shine, Fair-er still the moon-light,

O Thou of God and man the Son, Thee will I cher-ish,
Robed in the bloom-ing garb of spring; Je-sus is fair-er,
And all the twin-kling star-ry host; Je-sus shines bright-er,

Thee will I hon-or, Thou my soul's glo-ry, joy, and crown.
Je-sus is pur-er, Who makes the woe-ful heart to sing.
Je-sus shines pur-er, Than all the an-gels heav'n can boast.

92

The Sailboat

From the French

H. G. NÄGELI

LISTEN

Allegretto

SING

Come, drift in the sail-boat, Bright gleams the moon on high,
White, white is our sail-boat, Sweet, sweet is the feel of the foam,

LISTEN

SING

Fine

Swift, swift is the sail - boat, Smooth, smooth will it ply.——
Light, light is our sail - boat, Now bear - ing us home.——

LISTEN

SING

The wa-ters gleam with sil-ver light, The shore will soon be hid from sight;

The wa-ters gleam with light, —— The shore will soon be hid; ——

LISTEN

SING

D.C.

A chime of bells in dis - tance wells To mark the hour of night.

A chime —— of bells —— To mark the hour of night.

Song of the Lark

From the German

With joyful movement

MENDELSSOHN
Acc. by A.F.

LISTEN / SING

1. O lark, gai - ly sing, And her - ald the spring
2. In sum - mer's de - light, When val - ley and height

LISTEN

How sweet - ly thy glad notes are ris - ing!
With God's gra - cious gifts are a - bound - ing,

SING

To list to thy lay, I has - ten a - way,
Then tune - ful and clear, From far and from near,

LISTEN

The world's pet - ty tri - als de - spis - ing,
Thy song of thanks - giv - ing is sound - ing,

The world's pet-ty tri-als de-spis - ing.
Thy song of thanks-giv-ing is sound - ing.

Follow On!

(403B)

CANON

LISTEN

Allegro

SING

Come a-long, Sing a song, Fol-low me;
Do re mi mi fa sol fa mi re

Come a-long, Sing a song, Fol-low
Do re mi mi fa sol fa mi

It is eas-y, as you see. Ev-'ry day, In this
This is eas-y, too, you see. *Do re mi mi fa*

me; It is eas-y, as you see. Ev-'ry day,
re This is eas-y, too, you see. *Do re mi*

way Just re-peat Till the tune's com-plete.
sol Just re-peat Till the tune's com-plete.

In this way Just re-peat, com - plete.
mi fa sol Just re-peat, com - plete.

OLD SONG

The Sleepy Fishes
(303B)

SING

Allegro

1. Once I found a lit-tle boat, Such a pret-ty, pret-ty boat,
2. In the wa-ter, cool and deep, All the fish-es were a-sleep;
3. Said a her-ring to a trout, "We had bet-ter be a-bout;

LISTEN

Just as the sum-mer day was dawn-ing,
Then as the splash-ing gave them warn-ing,
Don't let a fish-er catch us yawn-ing."

SING

And I took a lit-tle oar, And I rowed a-way from shore,
Said a min-now to a skate, "Don't you lie a-bed so late,
Said a stur-geon to an eel, "Just im-ag-ine how I feel,

LISTEN

So ver-y, ver-y ear-ly in the morn-ing.
So ver-y, ver-y ear-ly in the morn-ing."
So ver-y, ver-y ear-ly in the morn-ing."

REFRAIN

SING

Ev-'ry mer-ry lit-tle wave-let had his night-cap on;

LISTEN

His light cap, bright cap, white cap on,

SING

Ev-'ry mer-ry lit-tle wave-let had his night-cap on,

LISTEN

So ver-y, ver-y ear-ly in the morn-ing.

96

Short'nin' Bread

(102B)

NEGRO FOLK SONG

1. Three li'l chil-lun ly-in' in bed, Two was sick an de oth-er 'most dead. Sent for de doc-tor an' de doc-tor said, Give dem ba-bies some short-'nin' bread.

2. Put on de skil-let, put on de led, Mam-my's gwine to make a li'l short-'nin' bread. Dat ain't all she's gwine to do, She's gwine to make a li'l cof-fee too.

Mam-my's li'l ba-by loves short-'nin', short-'nin', Mam-my's li'l ba-by loves short-'nin' bread. Mam-my's li'l ba-by love's short-'nin', short-'nin', Mam-my's li'l ba-by loves short-'nin' bread.

97

Mystic Number

OLD RHYME AUSTRIAN FOLK TUNE

Moderato

1. I count-ed in the heav-en, When the moon shed its light, White
2. White sheep grazed in the mead-ow, Ev-'ry one wore a bell; Each

stars that num-bered sev - en, They were twin-kling so bright.
one fol-lowed its shad-ow, O'er the grass where it fell.

I count-ed one, I count-ed two, I count-ed three, I count-ed
I count-ed one, I count-ed two, I count-ed three, I count-ed

four, I count-ed five, I count-ed six, I count-ed sev'n, Good-night!
four, I count-ed five, I count-ed six, I count-ed sev'n, Sleep well!

"The Swan" is one of a collection of pieces for orchestra called "Carnival of Animals" and written by the French composer, Saint-Saëns. It is one of the most beautiful of all melodies and is usually sung by the low-voiced cellos of the orchestra. Does it remind you of the graceful, unhurried movement of the swan, like a stately ship on the quiet water?

Andantino grazioso

Skip to My Lou
(202B)

Quick, easy movement

1. I've lost my girl, now what'll I do; I've lost my girl, now what'll I do;
Cho. Skip, skip, skip to my Lou, Skip, skip, skip to my Lou,

I've lost my girl, now what-'ll I do? Skip to my Lou, my dar-ling.
Skip, skip, skip to my Lou, Skip to my Lou, my dar-ling.

2. I'll get another,
   a better one too;

3. Can't get a redbird,
   a bluebird'll do;

4. Cat's in the buttermilk,
   skip to my Lou;

5. Flies in the sugar bowl,
   shoo, fly, shoo;

Formation: Single circle of partners, facing in. The girl is at her partner's right. An extra player (two or three in a large circle) is without a partner, inside the circle.

Action: All sing; they also clap in time to a verse started by the player in the center, who steals someone's partner and skips entirely around the circle back to her place. The player left without a partner immediately steals another. The skating position is usually taken by the couple, right hands joined, crossed by joined left hands.

Let Us Play a Gay Musette

(104B)   (2004A)

MAY SARSON

OLD FRENCH CAROL
Acc. by M.S.

1. Let us play a gay mu-sette, Sing-ing No-el, No-el, No-el,
2. Why is all this joy and mirth, Sing-ing No-el, No-el, No-el?

Ma-rie, Jean, and Co-lin-ette, Dance with steps as light as snow.
Je-sus Christ is born on earth, Child of Mar-y; Son of God.

Stars are danc-ing in the sky, Lights are danc-ing in the win-dows;
See this ti-ny Ba-by Boy; He has come to ban-ish sad-ness;

Voi-ces sing-ing in the street, In the air their ech-oes ring.
In His smile are peace and joy, Wel-come, too, for one and all.

Let us play a gay mu-sette, Sing-ing No-el, No-el, No-el,

Ma-rie, Jean, and Co-lin-ette, Dance with steps as light as snow.

DESIGN IN MUSIC

Do you like to see the shape of a sturdy tree, or of a passenger plane, or the lovely design of a sunflower bloom, or a piece of lace, or a snow crystal? Just as surely as there is interesting design in things which we can *see*, there is also design in *music* which we *hear* and *feel*.

Sometimes it is a rhythmic pattern of notes that comes over and over. Other times it is a tune exactly repeated, or changed just a little to surprise us. If you want to discover design in music, listen carefully for places where the music pauses, where it seems to breathe. Often these endings come quite regularly, like lines of a poem.

In some selections the music seems to divide into sections so neatly and regularly

that we can tell when the next ending will come—like the regular arches of a long bridge or the beautiful windows of a lovely church.

Sometimes one big section of the music is just right to balance the big section which came before it—like two chapters of a story.

One of the nicest designs in music, found often in our longer songs and instrumental selections, is formed by three big sections —the third like the first, and the middle section making a nice change from the first. It is a little like the good feeling of returning home again after a visit to a new place. See if you can hear this *three-part* design in the song on this page, or in Beethoven's "Minuet in G," or in the "Skye Boat Song" on page 168.

The Keeper

(202A)

ENGLISH FOLK SONG
Acc. by W. I.

With playful spirit and clean rhythm

1. The keep-er would a-hunt-ing go, And un-der his coat he
2. The first doe she did cross the plain; The keep-er fetched her
3. The sec-ond doe she crossed the brook; The keep-er fetched her

car-ried a bow, All for to shoot at a mer-rie lit-tle doe, A-
back a-gain; Where she is now she may re-main, A-
back with his hook, Where she is now you may go and look, A-

mong the leaves so green, O. Jack-ie boy! Mas-ter! Sing ye well? Ver-y well.

1st Voice   2nd Voice   1   2

Hey down! Ho down! Der-ry, der-ry down, A-mong the leaves so

green, O, To my hey down, down! To my ho down, down! Hey down! Ho down!

Der - ry, der-ry down, A - mong the leaves so green, O.

103

Frog Music
(303B)

GERTRUDE MANDER

HARVEY WORTHINGTON LOOMIS

LISTEN

There once was a frog Who jump'd in a bog, And played the bass

There once was a frog Who jump'd in a

fid-dle In the mid-dle Of a pud-dle; What a mud-dle!

bog, And played the bass fid-dle In the mid-dle Of a

SING   LISTEN

"Bet-ter go 'round! Bet-ter go 'round!"_____ His

pud-dle; What a mud-dle! "Bet-ter go 'round! Bet-ter go 'round!"____

mu-sic was short, For soon he was caught, And now in the mid-dle

His mu-sic was short, For soon he was caught,

Of a grid-dle He is fry-ing And is cry-ing:

And now in the mid-dle Of a grid-dle He is

104

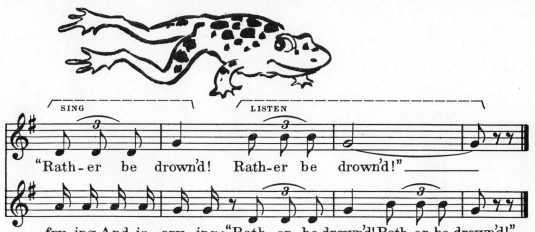

SING   LISTEN

"Rath-er be drown'd! Rath-er be drown'd!"

fry-ing And is cry-ing:"Rath-er be drown'd! Rath-er be drown'd!"

Learn this lively canon first as a song, then sing in two parts as indicated.

Early One Morning (404B)

OLD ENGLISH

With gentle movement

1.   Ear - ly one morn - ing, just as the sun was ris - ing,
2. Re - mem - ber the vows that you made to your Mar - y,
3. Oh, gay is the gar - land, and fresh are the ros - es
4. Thus sang the poor maid - en, her sor - row be-wail - ing,

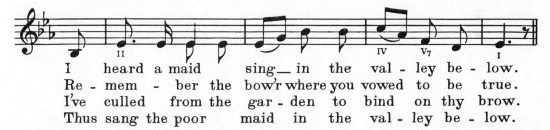

I heard a maid sing __ in the val - ley be - low.
Re - mem - ber the bow'r where you vowed to be true.
I've culled from the gar - den to bind on thy brow.
Thus sang the poor maid in the val - ley be - low.

CHORUS

mf

Oh! don't de - ceive me, Oh! nev - er leave me,

How could you use __ a poor maid - en so?

105

Bring a Torch, Jeannette, Isabella

(2001B)

Translation by
Miriam Hansen

OLD FRENCH CAROL
Acc. by W. I.

mp *Gently, with one light pulse per measure*

1. Bring a torch, Jean-nette, Is - a - bel - la, Bring a
2. Qui - et - ly, good folk of the ham - let, Soft - ly
3. Qui - et - ly, good folk of the vil - lage, Qui - et -

torch to the cra - dle small! See 'tis Je - sus, good
now, to the cra - dle come! Mute your voic - es, for
ly, for a mo - ment, come! See how charm - ing our

folk of the ham - let! Christ is born, and Mar - y
Je - sus is sleep - ing, An - gels a - bove Him watch are
lit - tle Sav - iour, Pink and white His cheeks, like

106

call - eth. Ah! Ah!
keep - ing. Hush! Hush!
ros - es. Sleep, Sleep,

Beau - ti - ful is His moth - er!
Do not dis - turb His slum - ber!
May your dreams be peace - ful.

Ah! Ah! Beau - ti - ful is her Boy!
Hush! Hush! Love - ly the sleep - ing Child!
Sleep, Sleep, Sleep now, dear lit - tle One.

TRADITIONAL

(301B) *Billy Boy*

AMERICAN FOLK SONG
Acc. by W. I.

LISTEN   SING

Touch   clap   touch   clap touch   clap touch   clap

1. Oh,   where   have you been, Bil-ly Boy, Bil-ly Boy,
2. Did she bid you to come in, Bil-ly Boy, Bil-ly Boy,
3. Did she set for you a chair, Bil-ly Boy, Bil-ly Boy,
4. Can she make a cher-ry pie, Bil-ly Boy, Bil-ly Boy,

LISTEN   SING

Touch   clap   touch   clap   touch   clap   touch clap

Oh,   where   have you been, charm-ing Bil-ly?
Did she bid you to come in, charm-ing Bil-ly?
Did she set for you a chair, charm-ing Bil-ly?
Can she make a cher-ry pie, charm-ing Bil-ly?

LISTEN   SING

Touch   clap   touch   clap touch   clap   touch   clap

I have been to seek a wife, She's the joy   of my life,
Yes, she bade me to come in, There's a dim-ple in her chin,
Yes, she set for me a chair, She has ring-lets in her hair,
She can make a cher-ry pie, Quick's a cat can wink her eye,

LISTEN

Touch   clap   touch   clap   touch   clap   touch clap

She's a young thing and can-not leave her moth-er.

108

Quaker's Wife

MAY SARSON

OLD SCOTTISH SONG

1. The quak-er's wife sat down to bake With all her bairns a-
2. The quak-er's wife sat down to spin And mer-ri-ly turned the

bout her. She made them all a sug-ar cake, And the
wheel oh! And then the quak-er he looked in To

mil-ler he wants his *mout-er. Sug-ar and spice and
say he'd like a meal oh! For if you feed your

all things nice, And all things ver-y good in it; And
good man well He'll love you all your life oh! And

then the quak-er sat down to play A tune up-on the spin-et.
then to all the world he'll tell There nev-er was such a wife oh!

CHORUS

Mer-ri-ly danced the quak-er's wife and mer-ri-ly danced the quak-er.

Mer-ri-ly danced the quak-er's wife and mer-ri-ly danced the quak-er.

*Fee in grain paid to miller

Camptown Races

(404A)

STEPHEN FOSTER

STEPHEN FOSTER
Acc. by W. I.

LISTEN *Lively* — SING

1. De Camp-town la - dies sing dis song, Doo-dah! doo-dah!
2. De long-tail fil - ly and de big black hoss, Doo-dah! doo-dah!
3. See dem fly-in' on a ten-mile heat, Doo-dah! doo-dah!

LISTEN — SING

De Camp-town race track five miles long, Oh! doo-dah day!
Dey fly de track and dey both cut a-cross, Oh! doo-dah day!
Round de race track den re - peat, Oh! doo-dah day!

LISTEN — SING

I come down dah wid my hat caved in, Doo-dah! Doo-dah!
De blind hoss stick-in' in a big mud hole, Doo-dah! Doo-dah!
I win my mon-ey on de bob-tail nag, Doo-dah! Doo-dah!

LISTEN ... SING

I go back home wid a pock-et full of tin, Oh! doo-dah
Can't touch de bot-tom wid a ten - foot pole, Oh! doo-dah
I keep my mon-ey in a old tow bag! Oh! doo-dah

LISTEN ... SING ... LISTEN

day!
day! Gwine to run all night! Gwine to run all day! I'll
day!

SING

bet my mon-ey on de bob-tail nag. Some-bod-y bet on de bay.

When the Little Children Sleep

(203B)

Arr. from Reinecke

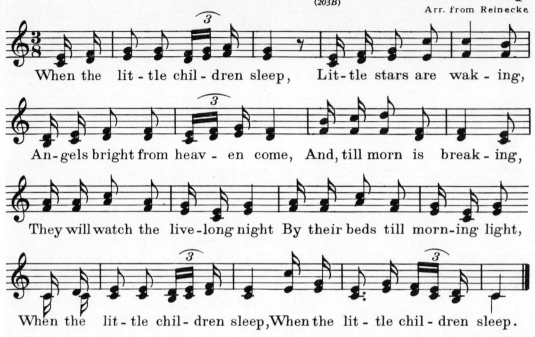

When the lit-tle chil-dren sleep, Lit-tle stars are wak-ing,

An-gels bright from heav-en come, And, till morn is break-ing,

They will watch the live-long night By their beds till morn-ing light,

When the lit-tle chil-dren sleep, When the lit-tle chil-dren sleep.

Choral Grace

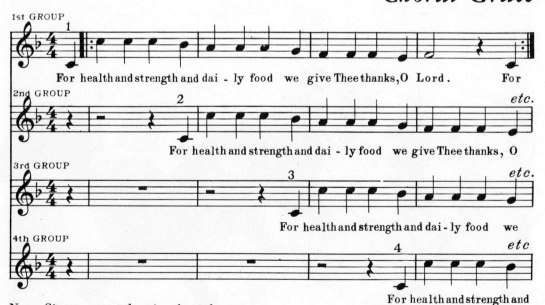

1st GROUP

For health and strength and dai-ly food we give Thee thanks, O Lord. For

2nd GROUP

etc.

For health and strength and dai-ly food we give Thee thanks, O

3rd GROUP

etc.

For health and strength and dai-ly food we

4th GROUP

etc.

For health and strength and

Note: Sing as a round, twice through

Crystal Day
(103B)

ENGLISH FOLK TUNE

LISTEN
Allegretto
SING
LISTEN

S d d d t d r S r r r d r m S m m

1. Come, 'tis a rare crys-tal day; Ice jew-els soon melt a-way. Come for a
2. Rich daz-zling sights meet the eye; Star flow'rs that fell from the sky, Dia-monds that

SING
LISTEN
SING

m r m f S l t d S s s s f s l S f f

gay win-ter play Here with Jack Frost! Mag-ic the gems that you see, Each blade of
gold ne'er could buy, Shine on the way. Come, ere they melt in the sun! See what the

LISTEN
SING

f m f s S m m m r m f S l t d

grass on the lea, Each ti-ny twig on the tree, Sil-ver em-bossed.
fay-folk have done, Spilled all these gems just for fun! Rare crys-tal day!

Yes! or No!
(302A)

MAY SARSON

HUNGARIAN AIR

LISTEN
SING

Loud soft loud soft loud soft loud soft loud soft loud soft loud soft loud soft

1. Daugh-ter dear, 'Tis the year You should wed; Have you thought Twice of aught You have said?
2. Moth-er dear, Have no fear, I shall wed Just the same One whose name I have said.

Do mi sol la fa re mi re do Do mi sol la fa re mi re do

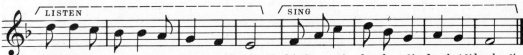

LISTEN
SING

loud soft loud soft loud soft loud soft loud soft loud soft loud soft loud soft

When you are read-y Your heart will show; Till that day Nev-er say Yes! or no!
Now I am read-y, My heart has shown, Should he press I'll say yes! Yes! a-lone.

La la sol fa fa mi re do ti Do mi sol la fa re mi re do.

Cielito Lindo

(103B)

English words
by M. G. F.

MEXICAN FOLK SONG
Acc. by W. I.

With graceful movement, one slow pulse per measure

mf SING

1. From Si-er-ras high—'neath a star-lit sky
2. The mag-ic white of the moon-lit night

—Comes my love-ly Cie - li-to Lin-do.—
—Shines on love-ly Cie - li-to Lin-do.—

LISTEN

Thru the gate—where the danc-ers wait—Comes my
Spar-kling eyes greet-ing lov-ers sighs Danc-es

laugh-ing Cie - li - to Lin-do.—
laugh-ing Cie - li - to Lin-do.—

Ay, ay ay ay! ____ No time for sor-row,_With mu-sic sweet

__ for her danc-ing feet_She will glad-den hearts_for the mor-row.

MAY SARSON

The Farmer's Son

FINNISH FOLK AIR

1. When my dad-dy left me all a - lone
2. When I tried to milk my pret-ty cow
3. Soon my lit-tle calf be-gan to roam,
4. Sud-den-ly my puss-y spied a mouse,
5. Now I'm all a-lone and far from glad,

I took the horse and plough to be my own,
'Twas hard-er work than driv-ing an-y plough,
And so I bought a cat to stay at home,
She chased it from the dair-y and the house;
A - think-ing of my friends that I have had—

But what a lad was I! I could-n't drive a plough,
I took her to the mar-ket for to get a calf
A pret-ty lit-tle thing to sit be-side the fire—
The two of them they raced and scam-pered right a-way,
My horse and plough, my pret-ty cow, my calf and cat,

And so I sold the pair of them and bought a cow.
And such a sil-ly bar-gain made the neigh-bors laugh.
I thought that she would stay with me and nev-er tire!
I've nev-er seen my pret-ty puss-y since that day!
And oh! it's sad to think that that's the end of that!

Fa la la la la la, Fa la la la la la,

What a sil-ly lad was I! Fa la la la la la.

116

PEER GYNT SUITE

Peer Gynt was a Norwegian youth who ran away from his mountain home and had many strange adventures in distant places. Edward Grieg, Norway's great composer, described some of Peer's experiences in a series of pieces called the "Peer Gynt Suite."

Morning

Peer's wanderings took him to far-off Egypt. The quiet, flowing melody of "Morning" tells of the beauty of a desert sunrise as he watches the gradual awakening of day.

Death of Ase

This sad and solemn music describes the death of Peer's lonely mother, Ase, who waited in vain for his return.

Anitra's Dance

In a camp on the Arabian desert, the native chief honored Peer by having his own daughter, Anitra, dance for him this Oriental tune.

In the Hall of the Mountain King

When Peer sought shelter in a mountain cave, he was suddenly surrounded by an increasing number of underground trolls, or imps, who tormented and tried to kill him. Their wild dance is suddenly ended by the coming of dawn.

Frog Went A-Courting
(2203A)

Words collected by
Loraine Wyman

KENTUCKY FOLK SONG
Melody collected by
Howard Brockway
Acc. by W. I.

Lively

1. Frog went a-court-ing and he did ride, Rink-tum bod-y minch-y cam-bo,
2. He rode down by the mill-side door, Rink-tum bod-y minch-y cam-bo, To

Sword and buck-ler by his side, Rink-tum bod-y minch-y cam-bo.
hear his sad-dle squeak and roar, Rink-tum bod-y minch-y cam-bo.

Ki-man-ee-ro down to Cai-ro, Ki-man-ee-ro Cai-ro,

Strad-dle ad-dle lad-da bob-bo   lad-da bob-bo link-tum, Rink-tum bod-y minch-y cam-bo.

3. Who will make the wedding gown?
   Old Miss Rat from Pumpkin Town.

4. Where will the wedding breakfast be?
   Way down yonder in a hollow tree.

5. What will the wedding supper be?
   A fried mosquito and a roasted flea.

6. First came in was a bumble bee
   A fiddle buckled on his knee.

7. Next came in was a little flea
   To dance a jig for the bumble bee.

8. Next came in was a big black snake
   Passing around the wedding cake.

9. Next came in was a big black bug
   On his back was a whisky jug.

10. Next came in was a big Tom cat
    Swallowed up mouse and growled
    at the rat.

Oh, Susanna!

STEPHEN FOSTER   STEPHEN FOSTER

KEY OF F

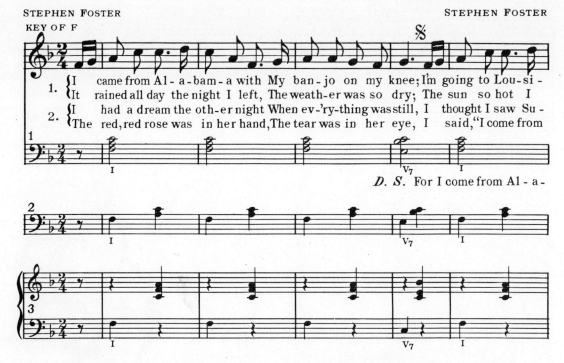

1. { I came from Al-a-bam-a with My ban-jo on my knee; I'm going to Lou-si-
   { It rained all day the night I left, The weath-er was so dry; The sun so hot I

2. { I had a dream the oth-er night When ev-'ry-thing was still, I thought I saw Su-
   { The red, red rose was in her hand, The tear was in her eye, I said, "I come from

D. S. For I come from Al-a-

Three patterns of simple chording for accompaniments.

Notice that with patterns 1 and 2 the melody is played with the right hand while the chording is done with the left. With

pattern 3 the melody is sung or whistled. Play the one you like best until you can do it easily, and then try that kind of chording with other songs.

The chords below will help you to find

For Songs in Key of C   For Songs in Key of B♭   For Songs in Key of E♭   For Songs in Key of A♭

I IV V₇ I   I IV V₇ I   I IV V₇ I   I IV V₇ I

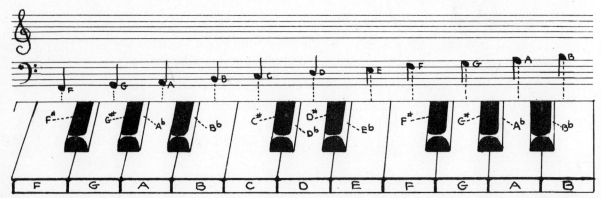

Fine.   *D. S.*

an - a, My Su-san-na for to see.
froze my-self Su-san-na don't you cry.
san-na come a - saunt-'ring down the hill.
Dix - ie-land, Su-san-na don't you cry.

Oh, Su-san-na! Oh, don't you cry for me,

1
I   I   V₇   I   IV   I   V₇

bam-a with my ban-jo on my knee.

2
I   I   V₇   I   IV   I   V₇

Fine.

3
I   I   V₇   I   IV   I   V₇

the right tones for songs in other keys. In chording, the first need is to select the right chord for that part of the tune. The Roman numerals will help you to know what chord is good. You will enjoy trying other combinations of the same tones which make up that chord. (Example: Any combination of C, E, G is numbered I in the Key of C.) See the classified index for list of songs marked for chording.

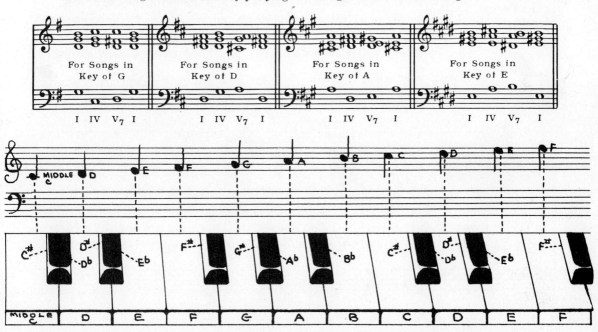

For Songs in
Key of G

For Songs in
Key of D

For Songs in
Key of A

For Songs in
Key of E

I IV V₇ I   I IV V₇ I   I IV V₇ I   I IV V₇ I

Away for Rio

(2202B)

With two pulses per measure

OLD SAILOR CHANTEY
Acc. by W. I.

mf LISTEN

1. O   the an-chor is weighed and the sails they are set;
2. We've a jol - ly good ship and a   jol - ly good crew;
3. Let us sing as we heave to the friends that we leave;
4. We will heave with a will   and heave stead-y and strong;

f SING   *mf* LISTEN

A - way   for Ri - o! The   town that we're leav-ing we'll nev-er for-get,
A - way   for Ri - o! A   jol - ly good mate and a   good skip-per too,
A - way   for Ri - o! They know at this part-ing how sad - ly we grieve,
A - way   for Ri - o! Come, sing a good cho-rus, for 'tis a good song,

For we're bound for Ri-o Grande.
For we're bound for Ri-o Grande.
For we're bound for Ri-o Grande.
For we're bound for Ri-o Grande.　So a - way　for Ri - o!　And aye　for

Ri - o!　Sing fare - ye - well for man - y　a day; We are bound for Ri - o　Grande!

The Bobolink
(403A)

M. LOUISE BAUM *Fleetly* ITALIAN FOLK SONG

LISTEN

1. Oh, the mer-ry bob-o'-link at brink of day, Hi!
2. Hear the stead-y stir and whir-ring of his wing, Hi!

SING

Sets the heart with-in me danc-ing, And I
As he wheels in diz-zy cir-cles, In his

long to fling a wing and sing a-way, Hi!
cap o' tan he's lead-er of the clan, Hi!

LISTEN

Far a-bove the mead-ow green. Far to climb, Ho!
And he wakes them up to sing. How the cho-rus

Heart a-chime, Ho! With the rous-ing song that calls us all to roam,
Ech-oes o'er us, Joy cas-cad-ing and in-vad-ing all with mirth,

SING

Those who dare, Ho! Ride the air, Ho! While the slug-gard lies at home.
Daft and daft-er, As with laugh-ter, Bob-o'-link's choir floods the earth.

Sweet Kitty Clover

KNIGHT

EDMUND KEAN

LISTEN

1.   Sweet Kit-ty Clo-ver, she both-ers me so,   Oh,
2. Sweet Kit-ty in per-son is rath-er low,   Oh, ____
3. If   Kit-ty to kirk   with me   would go,   Oh, ____

LISTEN

Oh, _____ Sweet Kit-ty Clo-ver, she both-ers me   so,
Oh, ____ Sweet Kit-ty in per-son is rath-er   low,
Oh, ____ If   Kit-ty to kirk   with me   would go,

SING   *LISTEN*

Oh, ____ Oh, Oh!   Her face   is round   and
Oh, ____ Oh, Oh!   She's three   feet tall,   and
Oh, ____ Oh, Oh!   I   think I should nev-er be

rit.

red   and fat, Like pul-pit cush-ion, or red-der than that; Oh,
that   I prize As just a fit height for a man of my size. Oh,
wretch-ed a-gain, If aft-er the par-son she'd say, "A-men?" Then

a tempo   *SING*

sweet Kit-ty Clo-ver, she both-ers me so,   Oh, __ Oh, __
sweet Kit-ty Clo-ver, you both-er me so,   Oh, __ Oh, __
Kit-ty would ne'er a-gain both-er me so,   Oh, __ Oh, Then

LISTEN   *SING*

Sweet Kit-ty Clo-ver, she both-ers me so,   Oh, __ Oh, Oh!
Sweet Kit-ty Clo-ver, you both-er me so,   Oh, __ Oh, Oh!
Kit-ty would ne'er a-gain both-er me so,   Oh, __ Oh, Oh!

125

Home on the Range

(2204A)

TRADITIONAL

COWBOY SONG
Arr. by I.W.

LISTEN

1. Oh, give me a home where the buf - fa - lo roam,
2. Where the air is so pure, the zeph-yrs so free,
3. How of - ten at night when the heav - ens are bright
4. Oh, I love these wild flow'rs in this dear land of ours,
5. Oh, give me a land where the bright dia-mond sand

SING

Where the deer and the an - te - lope play,
The breez - es so balm - y and light,
With the light from the glit - ter - ing stars,
The cur - lew I love to hear scream,
Flows lei - sure - ly down the stream;

LISTEN

Where sel - dom is heard a dis-cour-ag-ing word,
That I would not ex-change my home on the range
Have I stood here a-mazed and asked as I gazed
And I love the white rocks and the an - te-lope flocks
Where the grace-ful white swan goes glid-ing a - long

SING

And the skies are not cloud - y all day.
For all of the cit - ies so bright.
If their glo - ry ex - ceeds that of ours.
That graze on the moun - tain - tops green.
Like a maid in a heav - en - ly dream.

REFRAIN

SOP. LISTEN SING

ALTO

Home, home on the range; Where the deer and the an - te-lope play,

BAR.

126

Where sel-dom is heard a dis-cour-ag-ing word, And the skies are not cloud-y all day.

Texas Cowboy's Song
(204A)

TRADITIONAL

COWBOY SONG

With lazy motion

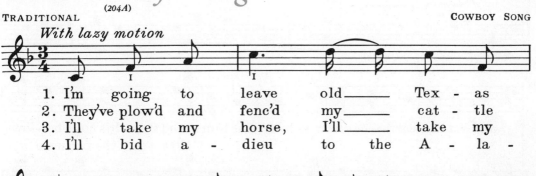

1. I'm going to leave old_____ Tex - as
2. They've plow'd and fenc'd my_____ cat - tle
3. I'll take my horse, I'll_____ take my
4. I'll bid a - dieu to the A - la -

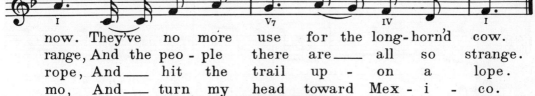

now. They've no more use for the long-horn'd cow.
range, And the peo - ple there are____ all so strange.
rope, And____ hit the trail up - on a lope.
mo, And____ turn my head toward Mex - i - co.

The Blacksmith
(404A)

W. A. MOZART

O the black-smith's a fine stur-dy fel-low, Hard his hand, but his heart's true and mel-low; See him stand there his huge bel-lows blow-ing, With his strong, brawn-y arms free and bare; See the

fire in the fur-nace a-glow-ing, Bright its spar-kle and flash, loud its blare.

2. Blow the fire, stir the coals, heaping more on,
Till the iron's all aglow, let it roar on!
While the smith high his hammer is swinging,
Fiery sparks fall in showers all around;
And the sledge on the anvil a-ringing,
Fills the air with its loud, clanging sound.

Cindy

(2203A)

APPALACHIAN FOLK SONG

With light rhythmic swing

SING

1. You ought to see my Cin-dy, She lives a-way down south,
2. She took me to the par-ler, She cooled me with her fan,
3. I wish I was an ap-ple, A-hang-ing in the tree,

LISTEN

She's so sweet the hon-ey bees Swarm a-round her mouth.
She swore that I's the purt-i-est thing In the shape of mor-tal man.
And ev-'ry time my sweet-heart passed, She'd take a bite of me.

SING

The first time that I saw her, She was stand-ing in the door,
She told me that she loved me, She called me sug-ar plum,
I wish I had a nee-dle, As fine as I could sew,

LISTEN

Her shoes and stock-ings in her hand And her feet all o-ver the floor.
She throwed 'er arms a-round me, I thought my time had come.
I'd sew the girls to my coat tail, And down the road I'd go.

SING LISTEN

Get a-long home, Cin-dy, Cin-dy, Get a-long home, Cin-dy, Cin-dy,

SING LISTEN

Get a-long home, Cin-dy, Cin-dy, I'll mar-ry you some-time.

Marianina
(403A)

DOROTHY LOGAN

With light easy movement

ITALIAN POPULAR SONG
Acc. by W. I.

1. Ma-ria-ni-na with the laugh-ing eyes, Sing-ing, danc-ing 'neath the
2. Ma-ria-ni-na, come and smile on me, Close your eyes a-gainst the

Tus-can skies; Sail-or lads who find you fair to see,
shin-ing sea; Love like this is rare as sun-set glow;

Ne'er can take you, love, from me, Ma-ria-ni-na, tra la la; Ma-ria-ni-na, tra la
Rich-er treas-ure none can know. Ma-ria-ni-na, tra la la; Ma-ria-ni-na, tra la

LISTEN, first time, SING, second time

la,   Ma - ria - ni - na, oh, Ma - ria
         Ma - ria - ni - na, oh, Ma - ria
la,   Ma - ria - ni - na, oh, Ma - ria
         Ma - ria - ni - na, oh, Ma - ria

ni - na,   Flow'rs en - twin - ing
ni - na,   Sing to me, my
ni - na,   My ra - diant Love, with
ni - na,   Sing - ing, danc - ing

1
in your rav - en hair,
laugh - ter in her eyes,

2
rose so wild and fair.
'neath the az - ure skies.

A GREAT AMERICAN

John Philip Sousa was known everywhere as the "March King of America."
For many years, his concert tours helped the people of America to know
how fine concert bands can be. He wrote many excellent marches, the most
popular being "The Stars and Stripes Forever."

The Stars and Stripes Forever

SOUSA

Florian's Song

M. LOUISE BAUM

BENJAMIN GODARD

mf *With flowing melody*

1. O tell me have you ev - er seen him?
2. Or if, when an - y poor man ven - ture
3. And if the mu - sic of his pip - ing

A shep-herd lad who smiles so bright That peo-ple
To beg a lamb from out the flock, The shep-herd
Shall charm the ver - y birds to hear, And if the

love him at first sight, And day by day still hold him dear - er?
does not spurn or mock, But gives both lamb and ewe to-geth - er,
maid who wan-ders near, Shall stay to list the sweet-ness sigh - ing,

f

That is my love, sure-ly 'tis he,
That is my love, no one but he,
That is my love, true un - til death,

poco rit.

I have his heart, my faith has he.
I have his heart, my faith has he.
I have his heart, and he my faith.

Sleigh Bells
(402A)

MAY SARSON

Light and fast

Russian Folk Tune "Minka"
Acc. by M.S.

1. Mer-ry bells go ting-a-lin-gle, Toes and fin-gers
2. As we ride our song goes ring-ing, Through the air its

freeze and tin-gle With our friends we gai-ly min-gle
ech-oes wing-ing, Till the world seems full of sing-ing:

While the snow-flakes fall. Boys and girls, come
So we speed a-long, Through the town and

out to-geth-er, Clad in coats of fur and leath-er
by the riv-er Where the bir-ches sigh and shiv-er

Made to brave the cold-est weath-er When the sleigh-bells ring.
And the birds are si-lent nev-er, Join-ing in our song.

(204B) Slumber Song

PORTUGUESE FOLK TUNE

1st SOP. *Allegro moderato*

2nd SOP.

1. Go to sleep my dar - ling, There's the eve-ning star; It was
2. Go to sleep my dar - ling, There's the ris-ing moon; She will

ALTO

Dar-ling go to sleep, There's the eve-ning
Dar-ling go to sleep, There's the ris-ing

light-ed by the an - gels, Who watch from a - far.
fill the field and for - est With light ver-y soon.

star; 'Twas light-ed by the an - gels a - far.
moon; 'Twill fill the woods with light ver - y soon.

Now All, Good Night

SOP. *Dolce* (303B)

ALTO

1. Now the qui-et shades are fall-ing, Soft-ly round our hum-ble dwell-ing,
2. Ho - ly an-gels' round us bend-ing, Peace on love's bright wings descending,
3. Hand in hand our path pur-su - ing, Day by day our joys re-new-ing,

BAR.

Sweet our eve-ning hymn is swell-ing, Now all, goodnight good night!
With our eve-ning wor-ship blend-ing, Now all, goodnight good night!
Here our words and deeds re-view-ing, Now all, goodnight good night!

134

The Volga Towing Path

M. LOUISE BAUM

RUSSIAN MELODY

With slow, sturdy rhythm

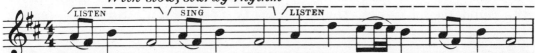

LISTEN SING LISTEN

1. Yo - heave ho, yo - heave ho! Heave and haul, boys, sure and slow.
2. Yo - heave ho, yo - heave ho! Vol - ga barg - es weigh we know!

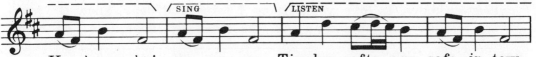

SING LISTEN

Yo - heave ho! up we go, Tim-ber rafts are safe in tow.
Yo - heave ho! in a row! Plod the path-way, bend-ing low.

SING

Moth-er Vol - ga sea-ward sweeps, Up stream how the tim-ber creeps!
Ropes are tug-ging, stiff and tight, Keep them taut, with all your might!

LISTEN SING

Haul all the hard-er, haul with a will! Vol-ga nev - er runs up hill.
Haul all the hard-er, haul with a will! Vol-ga nev - er runs up hill.

Franz Schubert lived only thirty-one years, but in his brief lifetime he
gave the world some of its greatest and most melodious music.
This "Moment Musicale" is a gem of gay melody and lively rhythm.

SCHUBERT

Allegro moderato

Down in the Valley
(103B)

AMERICAN FOLK SONG
Arr. by I. W.

1. Down in the val-ley, the val-ley so low, Hang your head o-ver, hear the wind blow. Hear the wind blow, dear, hear the wind blow, Hang your head o-ver, hear the wind blow.

2. Ros-es love sun-shine, vio-lets love dew, An-gels in heav-en know I love you; Know I love you, dear, know I love you, An-gels in heav-en know I love you.

3. Build me a cas-tle, for-ty feet high, So I can see him as he rides by; As he rides by, dear, as he rides by; So I can see him as he rides by.

A NOBLE MARCH BY A NOBLE COMPOSER

The festive ceremonies for the crowning of the King of England are unknown to us, but the majesty and noble melody of this march help us to imagine their grandeur.

ELGAR

Pomp and Circumstance

Molto maestoso

Dinah

(204A)

With lively spirit

Di-nah, won't you blow? Di-nah, won't you blow? Di-nah, won't you blow your horn? —

Di-nah, won't you blow? Di-nah, won't you blow? Di-nah, won't you blow your horn?

Some-one's in the kitch-en with Di-nah, Some-one's in the kitch-en I know. —

Some-one's in the kitch-en with Di-nah, Strum-min' on de old ban-jo.

Fee - fie - fid-dle-dee - i - o, Fee - fie - fid-dle-dee - i - o, _____

Fee - fie - fid-dle-dee - i - o, Strum-min' on de old ban-jo.

Are You Sleeping?

FRENCH ROUND

Moderato

1 LISTEN | SING | 2 LISTEN | SING | 3 LISTEN

Are you sleep-ing, are you sleep-ing, Broth-er John, broth-er John? Morn-ing

SING | 4 LISTEN | SING

bells are ring-ing, Morn-ing bells are ring-ing, Ding, ding, dong, ding, ding, dong

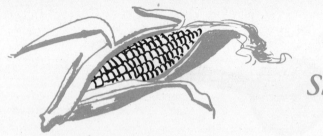

Shuckin' of the Corn

(202B)

TENNESSEE FOLK SONG
Acc. by W. I.

Fast, with spirit

LISTEN

1. I have a ship on the o - cean ___ All lined with
2. The wind blows cold in Cai - ro, ___ The sun re -

SING

sil - ver and gold, ___ Be - fore I'd see my
fus - es to shine, ___ Be - fore I'd see my

true love suf - fer, That ship should be an - chored and sold. ___
true love suf - fer, I'd work all the sum - mer time. ___

REFRAIN (*Second time, softly*)

LISTEN

I'm a-go-in' to the shuck-in' of the corn,———

——— I'm a-go-in' to the shuck-in' of the corn,———

SING

——— A-shuck-in' of the corn and a-blow-in' of the

horn, I'm a-go-in' to the shuck-in' of the corn.———

Sourwood Mountain

Collected by
Ralph Rigby

Lively movement

(301B)

KENTUCKY FOLK SONG
Acc. by W. I.

LISTEN   SING

1. Chick-en crow-ing on Sour-wood Moun-tain, Hey de ing dang did-dle al-ly day.
2. My true love's a blue-eyed dai-sy, Hey de ing dang did-dle al-ly day.
3. My true love lives up the riv-er, Hey de ing dang did-dle al-ly day.

LISTEN   SING

So man-y pret-ty girls I can't count 'em, Hey de ing dang did-dle al-ly day.
If I don't get her I'll go cra-zy, Hey de ing dang did-dle al-ly day.
A few more jumps and I'll be with her, Hey de ing dang did-dle al-ly day.

LISTEN   SING

My true love she lives in Letch-er, Hey de ing dang did-dle al-ly day.
Big dog bark and lit-tle one bite you, Hey de ing dang did-dle al-ly day.
My true love lives in the hol-low, Hey de ing dang did-dle al-ly day.

LISTEN   SING

She won't come and I won't fetch her, Hey de ing dang did-dle al-ly day.
Big girl'll court and lit-tle one'll slight you, Hey de ing dang did-dle al-ly day.
She won't come and I won't fol-low, Hey de ing dang did-dle al-ly day.

The Wakeful Brook

CZECHOSLOVAKIAN FOLK TUNE

Allegro moderato

SOP. *p* LISTEN

1. Soft - ly the shad - ows have quenched the day's light;
2. Blithe ran the brook - let, its task to ful - fill;
3. Shep - herds are si - lent - ly lead - ing their herds;

ALTO

SING

Moth - er has kiss'd her wee ba - by good - night.
All the day long it was turn - ing the mill.
Flow - ers are all lull'd to sleep by the birds.

LISTEN

Lull-a - by, oh, lull - a - by! Lull-a - by, oh, lull - a-by!

Lull - a - by! Lull - a - by!

2nd SOP.

ALTO

Lull-a-by, oh, lull - a - by! Lull-a-by, oh, lull - a - by!

SING

Tones that to slum - ber and dream-ing in - vite.
Now in the pool it sleeps, plac - id and still.
Sweet-est of all the fond songs with - out words.

141

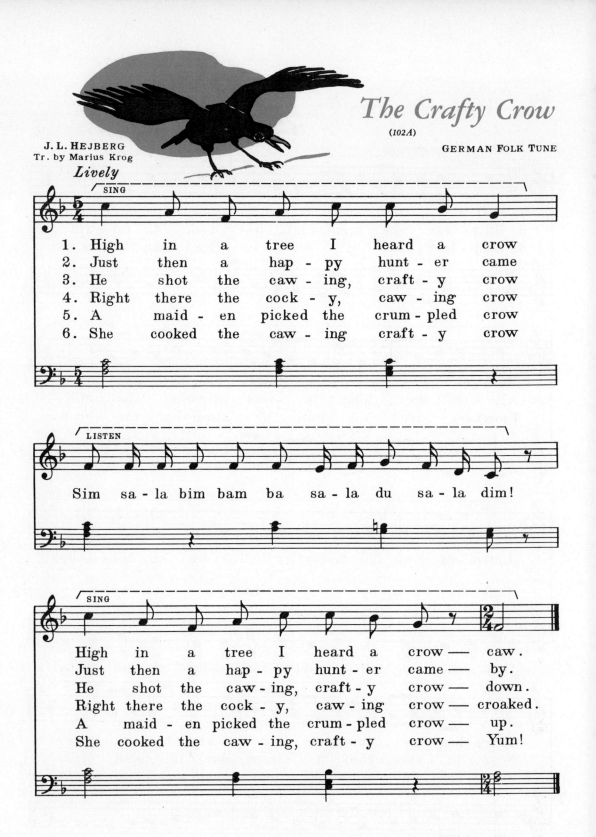

The Crafty Crow

(102A)

J. L. HEJBERG
Tr. by Marius Krog

GERMAN FOLK TUNE

Lively

SING

1. High in a tree I heard a crow
2. Just then a hap - py hunt - er came
3. He shot the caw - ing, craft - y crow
4. Right there the cock - y, caw - ing crow
5. A maid - en picked the crum - pled crow
6. She cooked the caw - ing craft - y crow

LISTEN

Sim sa - la bim bam ba sa - la du sa - la dim!

SING

High in a tree I heard a crow — caw.
Just then a hap - py hunt - er came — by.
He shot the caw - ing, craft - y crow — down.
Right there the cock - y, caw - ing crow — croaked.
A maid - en picked the crum - pled crow — up.
She cooked the caw - ing, craft - y crow — Yum!

Git Along, Little Dogies*

(102B)

TRADITIONAL
With two lazy swings per measure
COWBOY SONG

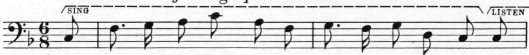

1. As   I   was a-walk-ing one morn-ing for pleas-ure, I
2. It's   ear-ly in Spring that we round up the do-gies, We
3. Some boys they go up   on the trail just for pleas-ure, But

spied a cow-punch-er all rid-ing a-long; His hat was throwed back and his
mark them and brand them and bob off their tails; We round up our hors-es, load
that's where they get it most aw-ful-ly wrong; You have-n't a   no-tion the

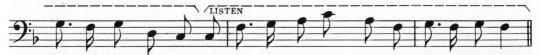

spurs were a-jin-gling, And as   he ap-proached he was sing-ing this song:
up   the chuck-wag-on, And then throw the do-gies out on-to the trail.
trou-ble they give us, It takes all our time   to keep mov-ing a-long.

Whoop-ee ti yi yo, git a-long, lit-tle do-gies, It's

your mis-for-tune and none of my own; Whoop-ee ti yi yo, git a-

long, lit-tle do-gies, You know that Wy-o-ming will be your new home.

Pronounced with long ō

Lullaby and Good Night

(303A)

JOHANNES BRAHMS

Quietly

SING / LISTEN

1. Lull - a - by and good-night! With ros - es be - dight,
2. Lull - a - by and good-night! Thy moth - er's de - light!

SING / LISTEN

With down o - ver - spread Is ba - by's wee bed.
Sweet vi - sions un - told Thy soul shall un - fold.

SING / LISTEN
poco cresc. / pp

Lay thee down now and rest, May thy slum-bers be blest;
God will keep thee from harms, Thou shalt wake in my arms;

SING / LISTEN
poco cresc. / pp rit.

Lay thee down now and rest, May thy slum - bers be blest.
God will keep thee from harms, Thou shalt wake in my arms.

The Linden Tree
WILHELM MULLER (303A)
FRANZ SCHUBERT

1. Be - side the rip-pling stream - let There stands a lin-den tree,
2. And if to-day I wan - der In oth - er lands a - far,
3. Tho' cold the winds, un-ceas - ing, Up - on my path-way roar,

Where dream-ing in its shad-ow, My hours were sweet and free; It's bark is
I close my eyes and pon-der Be-neath the eve-ning star, And hear those
Still on-ward I am go-ing, And can re-turn no more. Now years have

cut with let - ters From man-y fan-cies made; In joy and sor-row
branch-es mur - mur, As if they called to me: Come back and rest, com-
come and van-ished Since I be-held that tree, But still I hear it

ev - er I sought its grate-ful shade, I sought its grate-ful shade.
pan - ion, Be - neath the lin-den tree! Be - neath the lin-den tree!
whis-per: Come back and rest with me! Come back and rest with me.

Calling Me Back Home
(302A)

MAY SARSON

MAY SARSON
(Dedicated to my friend
C. A. Fullerton)

Smoothly, with warm feeling

1. There's a land, love-ly land Where the fir-trees grow.—
2. Friends are here, kind and dear; Skies are wide and blue;—

Sil - ver streams through my dreams Mur - mur as they flow.
O - ver there moun-tains wear Clouds of mist - y hue.

Though I stay far a-way I can hear by night and day
E - ven so, though I go All a-round the world, I know

slight slowing

Low - ing herds, songs of birds Call - ing me back home.
Loved ones there say a prayer Wish-ing me back home.

146

CONTRAST IN MUSIC

If you are like other boys and girls, you truly enjoy the changes that rest you from what otherwise might be very tiresome. A change that makes a real difference, like play after a period of hard work or springtime after a long winter, is called a *contrast*.

One reason music is so enjoyable is that it is full of *contrasts*. Instead of continuing for a long time in one way, it changes and moves very differently. How many kinds of changes have you noticed—changes that make real contrasts? Here are a few that boys and girls hear as they sing or play or listen:

From loud to soft, or soft to loud.
From fast to slow, or slow to fast.
From a steady rate to a speeding up or slowing down.
From one tune to two tunes that fit together.
From a solo voice or instrument to many of them together.
From a melody all by itself to a melody with accompaniment or a melody that is harmonized.
From a minor key to a major key.
From one kind of instrument to another, as from strings to brass.
From a smooth, flowing manner to a disconnected way of singing or playing.
From a short idea to a long, majestic idea like the view seen from high mountains.

Music is not all the same. It is fun to notice the changes. If you learn to hear and feel the *contrasts* in music you will always find it fresh and interesting and full of surprises.

When I Was a Lad
(204A)

W. S. GILBERT   (SIR JOSEPH)   SIR ARTHUR SULLIVAN
             Acc. by I. W.

In fun, with lively patter

1. When I was a lad I served a term As of-fice boy for an at-tor-ney's firm; I cleaned the win-dows and I swept the floor, And I pol-ish'd up the han-dle of the big front door. He

2. As of-fice boy I made such a mark That they gave me the post of a jun-ior clark; I served the writs — with a smile so bland, And I cop-ied all the let-ters in a big round hand. He

3. Now lands-men all, who-ever you may be, If you want to rise to the top of the tree, If your soul isn't fet-tered to an of-fice stool, Be care-ful to be guid-ed by this gold-en rule: Be

(CHORUS)

148

pol-ished up the han-dle of the big front door. I   pol-ish'd up the han-dle so
cop-ied all the let-ters in a   big round hand. I   cop-ied all the let-ters in a
care-ful to be guid-ed by this gold-en   rule: Stick close   to your desks and nev-er

(CHORUS)

care - ful - lee, That now I am the rul- er   of the Queen's Na-vee, He
hand   so free, That now I am the rul- er   of the Queen's Na-vee, He
go   to sea, And you all may be rul- ers of the Queen's Na-vee, Stick

cresc.

pol-ish'd up the han-dle so   care-ful-lee, That
cop-ied all the let-ters in a   hand so free, That
close   to your desks   and   nev-er go to sea, And

now he is the rul- er of the Queen's Na-vee.
now he is the rul- er of the Queen's Na-vee.
you all may be rul-ers of the Queen's Na-vee.

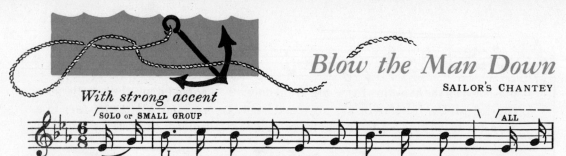

Blow the Man Down

SAILOR'S CHANTEY

With strong accent

SOLO or SMALL GROUP ... ALL

1. Come, all ye young fel-lows that fol-low the sea, With a
2. On board the Black Ball-er I first served my time, With a
3. There were tink-ers and tai-lors and sail-ors and all, With a
4. 'Tis lar-board and star-board, you jump to the call, With a

SOLO or SMALL GROUP

yeo-ho! we'll blow the man down! And please pay at-ten-tion and
yeo-ho! we'll blow the man down! And in the Black Ball-er I
yeo-ho! we'll blow the man down! That shipp'd for good sea-men on
yeo-ho! we'll blow the man down! When Kick-ing Jack Wil-liams com-

ALL

lis-ten to me, Give us some time to blow the man down!
wast-ed my time, Give us some time to blow the man down!
board the Black Ball, Give us some time to blow the man down!
mands the Black Ball, Give us some time to blow the man down!

Kookaburra

M. SINCLAIR

very fast

(202A) AUSTRALIAN ROUND

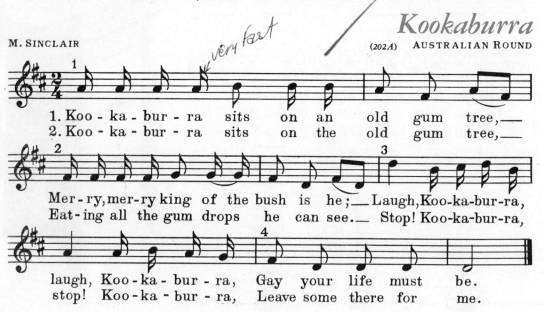

1. Koo-ka-bur-ra sits on an old gum tree,—
2. Koo-ka-bur-ra sits on the old gum tree,—

Mer-ry, mer-ry king of the bush is he;— Laugh, Koo-ka-bur-ra,
Eat-ing all the gum drops he can see.— Stop! Koo-ka-bur-ra,

laugh, Koo-ka-bur-ra, Gay your life must be.
stop! Koo-ka-bur-ra, Leave some there for me.

Springfield Mountain

(202B)

(According to George Pullen Jackson,
based upon real incident in Springfield
Outer Commons [Mass.] in 1761.)

APPALACHIAN MOUNTAIN BALLAD
Heard near Cookville, Tenn.

On Spring-field Moun-tain there did dwell A lov-li
One day this lov-li youth did go Down to the
He scarce had mow'd half 'round the field When cru-el
They tuck him home to Mol-li dear For he did
O John-i dear, why did you go Down to the
Why Mol-li dear, I thought you know'd The field was
Now Mol-li dear had ru-by lip With which the
But Mol-li dear had a rot-ting tooth And so the

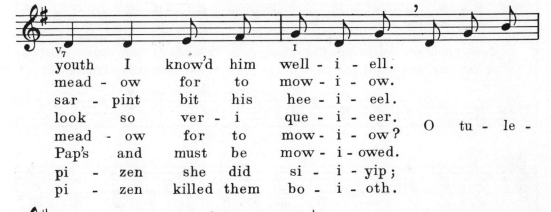

youth I know'd him well - i - ell.
mead - ow for to mow - i - ow.
sar - pint bit his hee - i - eel.
look so ver - i que - i - eer. O tu-le-
mead - ow for to mow - i - ow?
Pap's and must be mow - i - owed.
pi - zen she did si - i - yip;
pi - zen killed them bo - i - oth.

lu - ri - lu - ri - lay, O tu-le - lu - ri - lu - ri - lay.

Beautiful Dreamer

(2204B)

STEPHEN FOSTER

With easy flowing movement

STEPHEN FOSTER
Arr. by I.W.

1. Beau-ti-ful dream-er, wake un-to me, Star-light and dew-drop are wait-ing for Thee,— Sounds of the rude world heard in the day, Lull'd by the moon-light have all passed a-way— Beau-ti-ful dream-er, queen of my song,

2. Beau-ti-ful dream-er, out on the sea, Mer-maids are chant-ing the wild lor-e-lei;— O-ver the stream-let va-pors are borne, Wait-ing to fade at the bright com-ing morn.— Beau-ti-ful dream-er, beam on my heart,

De Glendy Burk

(2204B)

STEPHEN FOSTER   STEPHEN FOSTER

1. De Glen-dy Burk is a might-y fast boat, Wid a might-y fast cap-tain   too;
2. De Glen-dy Burk has a fun-ny old crew And dey sing   de boat-man's song,
3. I'll work all night in de wind   and storm, I'll   work   all day in de rain;

He   sits up dah on de hur-ri-cane roof And he keeps his eye on de crew.
Dey   burn de pitch and de pine knot too For to shove de boat a - long.
Till I   find my-self on de lev - y - dock In   New Or-leans a - gain.

I   can't stay here, for dey work too hard; I'm bound to   leave dis town;
De smoke goes up and de   in-gine roars And de wheel goes round and round;
Dey make me mow in de hay-field here And knock my   head wid de flail;

I'll   take my duds and   tote 'em on my back When de Glen-dy Burk comes down.
So   fare you well for I'll take a lit-tle ride When de Glen-dy Burk comes down.
I'll   go wha dey work wid de sug-ar and de cane And roll on de cot-ton bale.

Ho! for Lou'- si - an-a! I'm bound   to leave dis town; I'll take my duds and

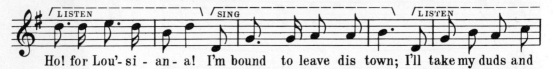

tote 'em on my back When de Glen-dy Burk comes down.

Jeanie with the Light Brown Hair

STEPHEN FOSTER   STEPHEN FOSTER

1. I dream of Jean-ie with the light brown hair, Borne like a va - por
2. I long for Jean-ie with the day-dawn smile, Ra-diant in glad-ness,
3. I sigh for Jean-ie, but her light form strayed Far from the fond hearts

on the sum-mer air; I see her trip-ping where the bright streams play,
warm with win-ning guile, I hear her mel-o - dies, like joys gone by,
'round her na-tive glade, Her smiles have van-ished and her sweet songs flown,

Hap-py as the dai - sies that dance on her way. Man-y were the
Sigh-ing 'round my heart o'er the fond hopes that die. Sigh-ing like the
Flit-ting like the dreams that have cheered us and gone. Now the nod-ding

wild notes her mer-ry voice would pour, Man-y were the blithe birds that
night wind and sob-bing like the rain, Wail-ing for the lost one that
wild flow'rs may with-er on the shore, While her gen-tle fin - gers will

war - bled them o'er. Oh! I dream of Jean - ie with the
comes not a - gain. Oh! I long for Jean - ie and my
cull them no more. Oh! I sigh for Jean - ie with the

light brown hair, Float-ing like a va-por, on the soft sum-mer air.
heart bows low, Nev - er more to find her where the bright wa-ters flow.
light brown hair, Float-ing like a va-por, on the soft sum-mer air.

Ay, Ay, Ay

English Words
by M. G. F.

(102B) CREOLE SONG
Acc. by W. I.

Dreamily

LISTEN   SING

1. I bring you in song my love, ay, ay, ay, O list to my mu-sic's sweet tune. The
2. The clouds hide the moon's white glow, ay, ay, ay, The bay-ou is dark-ened by night. The

LISTEN   hold   in time   SING

stars bright-ly gleam far a - bove, ay, ay, ay, Their light with the dawn will fade soon. My
wind thru the trees whis-p'ring low, ay, ay, ay, Is seek-ing your win-dow's soft light. I

LISTEN   SING

heart is sing-ing its song to you, Re-mem-b'ring al-ways our vows so true, Oh
hear the sound of your voice so dear, I dream of days with you ev-er near, Oh

LISTEN   hold   in time   SING

tell me your love will ne'er die, ay, ay, ay, O tell me your love will ne'er die.
tell me my dream will ne'er die, ay, ay, ay, O tell me my dream will ne'er die.

156

Spirit of Summertime

(404B)

WILLIAM ALLINGHAM

IRISH FOLK SONG
Arr. by I.W.

SOP.

ALTO

1. Oh spir-it sweet of sum—mer time,
2. Bring back the sing-ing, bring the scent

BAR.

Bring back the ros-es to ___ the dells,
Of mead-ow lands at dew___ y prime;

The swal-low from her dis___ tant clime,
Oh! bring a-gain my heart's___ con-tent,

slight slowing

The hon-ey bee from drow-sy cells.
Thou spir-it sweet of sum—mer time.

In Derry Vale
(302A)

W. G. ROTHERY

LONDONDERRY AIR
Acc. by W. I.

1. In Der-ry Vale, be-side the sing-ing riv-er, So oft I strayd, ah, man-y years a - go, And cull'd at morn the gold-en daf-fo-dil - lies That came with spring to set the world a - glow. Oh, Der-ry Vale, my tho'ts are ev - er turn-ing To your broad stream and fai-ry cir-cled

2. In Der-ry Vale, a-mid the Foyle's dark wa-ters, The sal-mon leap a-bove the surg-ing weir, The sea-birds call, I still can hear them call-ing In night's long dreams of those so dear. Oh, tarry-ing years, fly fast-er, ev-er fast - er, I long to see the vale be-lov'd so

lea, _____ For your green isles my ex - iled heart is
well, _____ I long to know that I am not for -

yearn - ing, So far a - way ____ a - cross the sea.
got - ten, And there at home ____ in peace to dwell.

RONDINO

This charming little melody, originally written by Beethoven, was used by the great violinist-composer Kreisler as the theme for his "Rondino," or little rondo.

In a rondo the main theme or melody comes over and over, with very different tunes in between for contrast. It is like a game where all go around the circle together, then someone does something in the center, after which all move around together again; then after a still different activity, everyone goes around the circle as at first. In music, this idea of returning to the first familiar tune after hearing something quite different is used in many types.

See if you can recognize the main tune each time it comes. When you are sure you can, then notice how interesting the contrast sections are.

RONDINO   BEETHOVEN

My Love's an Arbutus

ALFRED PERCEVAL GRAVES

IRISH FOLK SONG

1. My love's an ar-bu-tus By the bor-ders of
2. But tho' rud-dy the ber-ry And snow-y the
3. A-las, fruit and blos-som Shall lie dead on the

Lene, So slen-der and shape-ly In her gir-dle of
flow'r That bright-en to-geth-er The ar-bu-tus
lea, And time's jeal-ous fin-gers Dim your young charms, Ma-

green, And I meas-ure the pleas-ure of her eyes' sap-phire
bow'r, Per-fum-ing and bloom-ing Thru sun-shine and
chree, But un-rang-ing, un-chang-ing, You'll still cling to

sheen By the blue skies that spar-kle Thru the soft branch-ing screen.
show'r, Give me her bright lips And her laugh's pearl-y dow'r.
me, Like the ev-er-green leaf To the ar-bu-tus tree.

Bendemeer's Stream

(404A)

Thomas Moore

Irish Folk Song
Acc. by W. I.

mp

SING

1. There's a bow-er of ros-es by Ben-de-meer's stream, And the night-in-gale
   In the time of my child-hood 'twas like a sweet dream To sit in the

2. No, the ros-es soon with-er'd that hung o'er the wave, But some blos-soms were
   And the dew was dis-till'd from their flow-ers that gave All the fra-grance of

LISTEN

SING

sings round it all the day long.
ros-es and hear the bird's song. That bow'r and its mu-sic I ne'er shall for-get But
gath-er'd while fresh-ly they shone.
sum-mer when sum-mer is gone. Thus mem-o-ry draws from de-light ere it dies An

LISTEN

SING

oft when a-lone in the bloom of the year, I think, "Is the night-in-gale
es-sence that breathes of it man-y a year; Thus bright to my soul, as 'twas

LISTEN

sing-ing there yet? Are the ros-es still bright by the calm Ben-de-meer?"
then to my eyes, Is that bow-er on the banks of the calm Ben-de-meer!

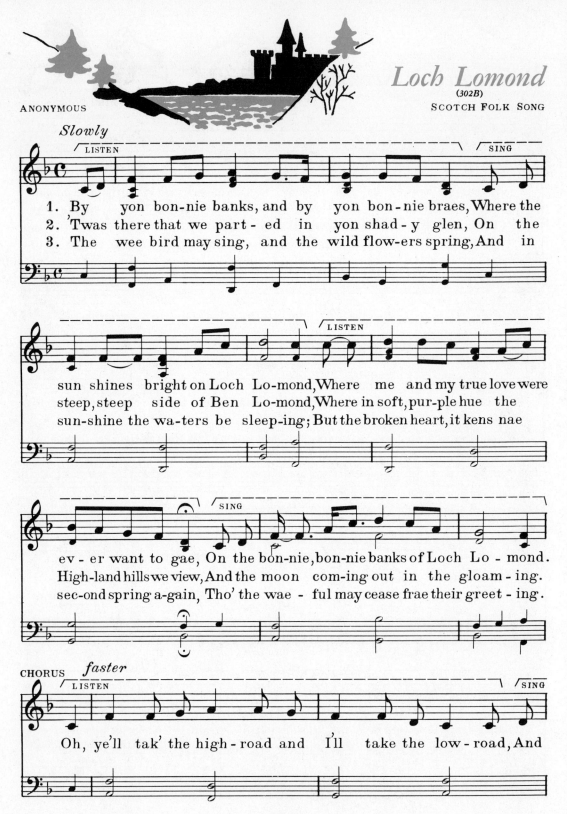

Loch Lomond
(302B)

ANONYMOUS

SCOTCH FOLK SONG

Slowly

LISTEN   SING

1. By yon bon-nie banks, and by yon bon-nie braes, Where the
2. 'Twas there that we part-ed in yon shad-y glen, On the
3. The wee bird may sing, and the wild flow-ers spring, And in

LISTEN

sun shines bright on Loch Lo-mond, Where me and my true love were
steep, steep side of Ben Lo-mond, Where in soft, pur-ple hue the
sun-shine the wa-ters be sleep-ing; But the broken heart, it kens nae

SING

ev-er want to gae, On the bon-nie, bon-nie banks of Loch Lo-mond.
High-land hills we view, And the moon com-ing out in the gloam-ing.
sec-ond spring a-gain, Tho' the wae-ful may cease frae their greet-ing.

CHORUS   **faster**

LISTEN   SING

Oh, ye'll tak' the high-road and I'll take the low-road, And

I'll be in Scot-land a - fore ye; But me and my true love will nev- er meet a-gain On the bon-nie, bon-nie banks of Loch Lo-mond.

GRACEFUL OLD DANCE OF DAINTY STEPS

The slow and stately minuet, written in ¾ time, was danced by the lords and ladies of the French court long ago in the 18th and 19th centuries. Two of the world's greatest composers wrote the following graceful melodies in this dance form:

Minuet from Don Juan   MOZART

Moderato

Minuet in G   BEETHOVEN

Allegretto (ma non troppo)

Weel May the Keel Row

(302B)

TRADITIONAL

SCOTCH FOLK TUNE

Very rapidly

1. As I cam' thro' Sand-gate, thru Sand-gate, thru Sand-gate, As
2. "He wears a blue bon - net, blue bon - net, blue bon - net, He

CHO. *Weel may the keel row, the keel row, the keel row,*

I cam' thro' Sand-gate, I heard a las-sie sing: "Weel may the keel row, the
wears a blue bon-net, A dim-ple in his chin." "Weel may the keel row, the

Weel may the keel row that my lad's in.

keel row, the keel row, Weel may the keel row, that my lad-die's in."
keel row, the keel row, Weel may the keel row, that my lad-die's in."

O Wert Thou in the Cauld Blast

ROBERT BURNS

FELIX MENDELSSOHN

1. O wert thou in the cauld blast On yon-der lea, on yon-der lea,
2. Or were I in the wild-est waste, Sae black and bare, sae black and bare,

My plaid-ie to the an-gry airt, Should shel-ter thee, should shel-ter thee!
The des-ert were a par - a - dise, If thou wert there, if thou wert there.

Or did mis-for-tune's bit-ter storms A-round thee blaw, a-round thee blaw,
Or were I mon-arch of the globe, With thee to reign, with thee to reign,

Thy shield should be my bos - om, To share it a', to share it a'.
The bright-est jew-el in my crown Wad be my Queen, wad be my Queen.

John Peel
(204B)

J. W. GRAVES

OLD ENGLISH
HUNTING SONG

With spirited movement

SOP.
ALTO

1. D'ye ken John Peel with his coat so gay, D'ye
2. Yes, I ken John Peel and Ru - by too!
3. Then here's to John Peel from my heart and soul, Let's

Cho. For the sound of his horn brought me from my bed, And the

BAR.

ken John Peel   at the break of the day, D'ye ken   John Peel
Ran-ter and Ring-wood Bell-man and True,From a find   to a check,
drink to his health, let's   fin-ish the bowl, We'll fol-low John Peel
cry of his hounds which he oft-times   led;   Peel's view hal-loo

when he's far, far   a-way,With his hounds and his horn in the morn-ing?
from a check to   a view,From a view to a death in the morn-ing.
thro'   fair and thro' foul, If we want a good hunt in the morn-ing.
would a-wak-en the dead, Or the fox from his lair in the morn-ing.

★ Observe the hold only in the chorus

Skye Boat Song
(302B)

HAROLD BOULTON

OLD HIGHLAND ROWING MEASURE

Speed, bon-nie boat, like a bird on the wing, On-ward, the sail-ors cry;

Car-ry the lad that's born to be king O-ver the sea to Skye. Skye.

1-2-3 Last

SING

rit. Fine.

SOLO *With energy*

LISTEN

1. Loud the winds howl, loud the waves roar, Thun-der-clouds rend the air;
2. Tho' the waves leap, soft shall ye sleep, O-cean's a roy-al bed.
3. Man-y's the lad fought on that day, Well the clay-more could wield,
4. Burn'd are our homes, ex - ile and death Scat-ter the loy-al men;

168

rit.   D. S.

SING

Baf-fled, our foes stand by the shore, Fol-low they will not dare.
Rock'd in the deep, Flo-ra will keep Watch by your wea-ry head.
When the night came, si-lent-ly lay Dead on Cul-lo-den's field.
Yet ere the sword cool in the sheath, Char-lie will come a-gain.

rit.

Drink to Me Only with Thine Eyes

BEN JONSON   OLD ENGLISH AIR

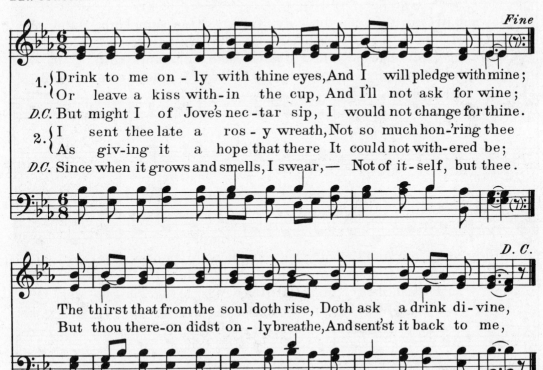

Fine

1. {Drink to me on-ly with thine eyes, And I will pledge with mine;
   {Or leave a kiss with-in the cup, And I'll not ask for wine;
D.C. But might I of Jove's nec-tar sip, I would not change for thine.

2. {I sent thee late a ros-y wreath, Not so much hon-'ring thee
   {As giv-ing it a hope that there It could not with-ered be;
D.C. Since when it grows and smells, I swear,— Not of it-self, but thee.

D. C.

The thirst that from the soul doth rise, Doth ask a drink di-vine,
But thou there-on didst on-ly breathe, And sent'st it back to me,

169

The Wraggle Taggle Gypsies

OLD ENGLISH

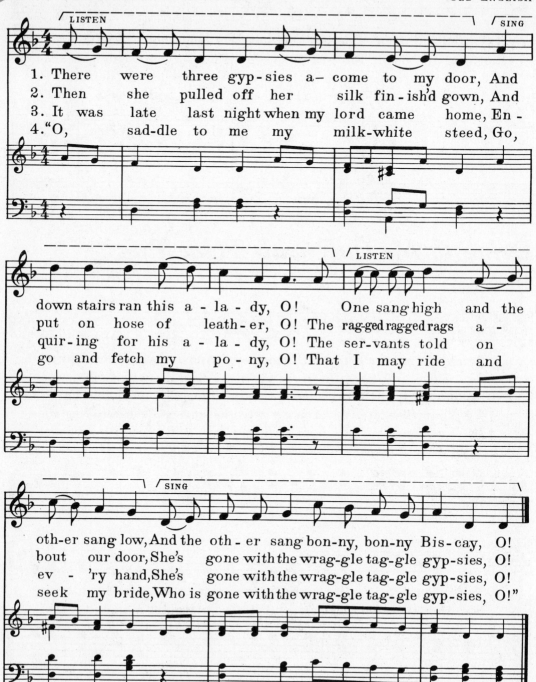

1. There were three gyp-sies a— come to my door, And down stairs ran this a - la - dy, O! One sang high and the oth-er sang low, And the oth - er sang bon-ny, bon-ny Bis-cay, O!

2. Then she pulled off her silk fin - ish'd gown, And put on hose of leath-er, O! The rag-ged rag-ged rags a - bout our door, She's gone with the wrag-gle tag-gle gyp-sies, O!

3. It was late last night when my lord came home, En-quir-ing for his a - la - dy, O! The ser-vants told on ev - 'ry hand, She's gone with the wrag-gle tag-gle gyp-sies, O!

4. "O, sad-dle to me my milk-white steed, Go, go and fetch my po - ny, O! That I may ride and seek my bride, Who is gone with the wrag-gle tag-gle gyp-sies, O!"

170

5. O he rode high and he rode low,
   He rode through woods and copses too,
   Until he came to an open field,
   And there he espied his a-lady, O!

Lord 6. What makes you leave your house and land?
   What makes you leave your money, O?
   What makes you leave your new wedded lord,
   To go with the wraggle taggle gypsies, O?

Lady 7. O what care I for my house and my land?
   What care I for my money, O?
   What care I for my new wedded lord?
   I'm off with the wraggle taggle gypsies, O.

Lord 8. Last night you slept on a goose-feather bed,
   With the sheet turned down so bravely? O!
   And to night you'll sleep in a cold open field,
   Along with the wraggle taggle gypsies, O!

Lady 9. What care I for a goose-feather bed,
   With the sheet turned down so bravely, O!
   For to night I shall sleep in a cold open field,
   Along with the wraggle taggle gypsies, O!

Now Is the Month of Maying

TRADITIONAL

THOMAS MORLEY

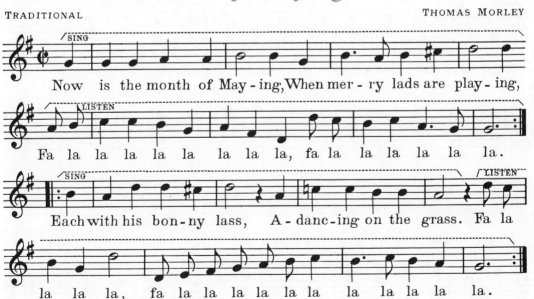

Now   is the month of May-ing, When mer-ry lads are play-ing,

Fa la   la   la   la   la   la la la, fa la   la la la la la.

Each with his bon-ny lass,   A-danc-ing on the grass. Fa la

la   la   la,   fa la la la la la la la   la la la la   la.

Annie Laurie

WILLIAM DOUGLASS

LADY JOHN SCOTT

Andante

1. Max - well - ton's braes are bon - nie, Where ear - ly fa's the dew,
2. Her brow is like the snow-drift, Her throat is like the swan,
3. Like dew on the gow - an ly - ing Is the fa' o' her fair - y feet,

And it's there that An - nie Lau - rie Gave me her prom - ise true.
Her face it is the fair - est That e'er the sun shone on.
And like winds in sum - mer sigh-ing, Her voice is soft and sweet,

Gave me her prom - ise true, Which ne'er for - got will be,
That e'er the sun shone on, And dark blue is her e'e,
Her voice is soft and sweet, And she's a' the world to me,

And for bon - nie An - nie Lau - rie I'd lay me doon and dee.

172

Wondrous Love
(104A)

SOUTHERN FOLK HYMN
Acc. by W. I.

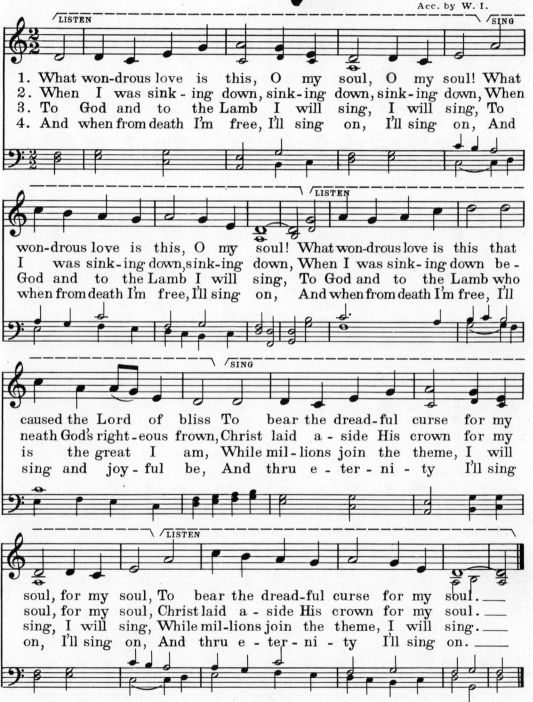

LISTEN · SING

1. What won-drous love is this, O my soul, O my soul! What
2. When I was sink-ing down, sink-ing down, sink-ing down, When
3. To God and to the Lamb I will sing, I will sing, To
4. And when from death I'm free, I'll sing on, I'll sing on, And

LISTEN

won-drous love is this, O my soul! What won-drous love is this that
I was sink-ing down, sink-ing down, When I was sink-ing down be-
God and to the Lamb I will sing, To God and to the Lamb who
when from death I'm free, I'll sing on, And when from death I'm free, I'll

SING

caused the Lord of bliss To bear the dread-ful curse for my
neath God's right-eous frown, Christ laid a-side His crown for my
is the great I am, While mil-lions join the theme, I will
sing and joy-ful be, And thru e-ter-ni-ty I'll sing

LISTEN

soul, for my soul, To bear the dread-ful curse for my soul.__
soul, for my soul, Christ laid a-side His crown for my soul.__
sing, I will sing, While mil-lions join the theme, I will sing.__
on, I'll sing on, And thru e-ter-ni-ty I'll sing on.__

Long, Long Ago

T. H. BAYLY

1. Tell me the tales that to me were so dear, Long, long a-go,
2. Do you re-mem-ber the paths where we met, Long, long a-go,
3. Tho' by your kind-ness my fond hopes were raised, Long, long a-go,

Long, long a-go; Sing me the songs I de-light-ed to hear,
Long, long a-go; Ah, yes, you told me you ne'er would for-get,
Long, long a-go; You, by more el-o-quent lips have been praised,

Long, long a-go, long a-go. Now you are come, all my
Long, long a-go, long a-go. Then, to all oth-ers my
Long, long a-go, long a-go. But by long ab-sence your

grief is re-moved, Let me for-get that so long you have roved,
smile you pre-ferr'd, Love, when you spoke, gave a charm to each word,
truth has been tried, Still to your ac-cents I lis-ten with pride,

LISTEN

Let me be - lieve that you love as you loved, Long, long a - go, long a - go.
Still my heart treas-ures the prais-es I heard, Long, long a - go, long a - go.
Blest as I was when I sat by your side, Long, long a - go, long a - go.

Auld Lang Syne

ROBERT BURNS

SCOTCH AIR

mf

1. Should auld ac-quaint-ance be for-got, And nev-er bro't to mind? Should
2. And here's a hand, my trust-y frien' And gie's a hand o' thine; We'll

auld ac-quaint-ance be for-got, And days of auld lang syne? For auld lang
tak' a cup o' kind-ness yet, For auld lang syne. For auld lang

syne, my dear, For auld lang syne; We'll tak' a cup o' kind-ness yet For auld lang syne.

Nobody Knows the Trouble I See

(2205B)

NEGRO SPIRITUAL

SOLO or SMALL GROUP ... CHORUS

Oh, no-bod-y knows the trou-ble I see, No-bod-y knows but Je-sus;

SOLO ... CHORUS ... *Fine.*

No-bod-y knows the trou-ble I see, Glo-ry hal-le-lu-ja!

DUET *somewhat faster* ... CHORUS

1. Some-times I'm up, some-times I'm down, Oh, yes, Lord!
2. Al-though you see me goin' 'long so, Oh, yes, Lord!
3. What makes old Sa-tan hate me so, Oh, yes, Lord!

DUET ... CHORUS *D. C. al Fine*

Some-times I'm al-most to the groun', Oh, yes, Lord!
I have my trou-bles here be-low, Oh, yes, Lord!
'Cause he got me once and let me go, Oh, yes, Lord!

176

Jacob's Ladder

(304B)

Deeply, broadly

NEGRO SPIRITUAL
Arr. by I.W.

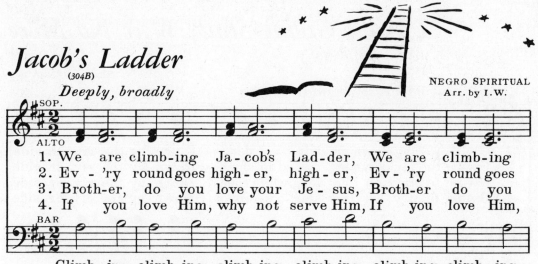

1. We are climb-ing Ja-cob's Lad-der, We are climb-ing
2. Ev-'ry round goes high-er, high-er, Ev-'ry round goes
3. Broth-er, do you love your Je-sus, Broth-er do you
4. If you love Him, why not serve Him, If you love Him,

Climb-ing, climb-ing, climb-ing, climb-ing, climb-ing, climb-ing,
High-er, high-er, high-er, high-er, high-er, high-er,
Love Him, love Him, love Him, love Him, love Him, love Him,
Serve Him, serve Him, serve Him, serve Him, serve Him, serve Him,

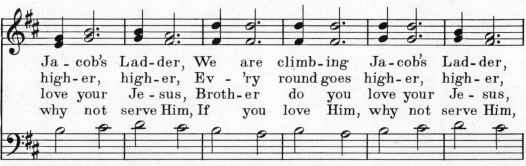

Ja-cob's Lad-der, We are climb-ing Ja-cob's Lad-der,
high-er, high-er, Ev-'ry round goes high-er, high-er,
love your Je-sus, Broth-er do you love your Je-sus,
why not serve Him, If you love Him, why not serve Him,

climb-ing, climb-ing, climb-ing, climb-ing, climb-ing, climb-ing,
high-er, high-er, high-er, high-er, high-er, high-er,
love Him, love Him, love Him, love Him, love Him, love Him,
serve Him, serve Him, serve Him, serve Him, serve Him, serve Him,

D. C. Last ending

Sol-diers of the Cross.
Sol-diers of the Cross.
Sol-diers of the Cross.
Sol-diers of the Cross.

climb-ing, climb-ing, climb-ing, climb-ing.
high-er, high-er, high-er, high-er.
love Him, love Him, love Him, love Him.
serve Him, serve Him, of the cross.

177

I Ain't Gwine Study War No More

1. Gwine to lay down my bur - den, Down by the riv-er-side,
2. Gwine to lay down my sword an' shiel', Down by the riv-er-side,
3. Gwine to try on my long white robe, Down by the riv-er-side,
4. Gwine to try on my star-ry crown, Down by the riv-er-side,

Down by the riv-er-side, Down by the riv-er-side;
Down by the riv-er-side, Down by the riv-er-side;
Down by the riv-er-side, Down by the riv-er-side;
Down by the riv-er-side, Down by the riv-er-side;

Gwine to lay down my bur - den, Down by the riv-er-side, to
Gwine to lay down my sword an' shiel', Down by the riv-er-side, to
Gwine to try on my long white robe, Down by the riv-er-side, to
Gwine to try on my star-ry crown, Down by the riv-er-side, to

stud-y war no more. I ain't gwine stud-y war no

Lord, I Want to Be a Christian

(304B)

NEGRO SPIRITUAL

Very simply

SOLO ALL

1. Lord, I want to be a Chris-tian in-a my heart, in-a my
2. Lord, I want to be more lov-ing in-a my heart, in-a my
3. Lord, I want to be more ho-ly in-a my heart, in-a my
4. Lord, I want to be like Je-sus in-a my heart, in-a my

DUET ALL

heart, Lord, I want to be a Chris-tian in-a my heart.
heart, Lord, I want to be more lov-ing in-a my heart.
heart, Lord, I want to be more ho-ly in-a my heart.
heart, Lord, I want to be like Je-sus in-a my heart.

In-a my heart, _____ In-a my heart, _____
In-a my heart, In-a my heart,

Lord, I want to be a Chris-tian in-a my heart.
Lord, I want to be more lov-ing in-a my heart.
Lord, I want to be more ho-ly in-a my heart.
Lord, I want to be like Je-sus in-a my heart.

Swing Low, Sweet Chariot

NEGRO SPIRITUAL

Swing low, sweet char-i-ot, Com-ing for to car-ry me home,

Swing low, sweet char-i-ot, Com-ing for to car-ry me home.

1. I looked o - ver Jor-dan, and what did I see, Com-ing for to car-ry me
2. If you get there be - fore I do, Com-ing for to car-ry me
3. The bright-est day that ev - er I saw, Com-ing for to car-ry me
4. I'm some-times up and some - times down, Com-ing for to car-ry me

home? A band of an - gels com-ing aft-er me, Com-ing for to car-ry me home.
home, Tell all my friends I'm com - ing too, Com-ing for to car-ry me home.
home, When Je-sus wash'd my sins a - way, Com-ing for to car-ry me home.
home, But still my soul feels heav'n - ly bound, Com-ing for to car-ry me home.

Deep River

NEGRO SPIRITUAL
Arr. by H.T. Burleigh

Without accent, but with rhythmic, even pulse

Deep ___ riv-er, my home is o-ver Jor-dan,

Deep ___ riv-er, Lord, I want to cross o-ver in-to camp-ground.

p a tempo

Deep ___ riv-er, my home is o-ver Jor-dan,

rit.

Deep ___ riv-er, Lord, I want to cross o-ver in-to camp-ground.

mf

Oh, don't you want to go ___ to that gos-pel feast, ___ That

f   *p*

prom-ised land where all is peace? Oh, deep ___

rit.

riv-er, Lord, I want to cross o-ver in-to camp-ground.

182

Santa Lucia

English Version by Eleanor Wynne

NEAPOLITAN SERENADE

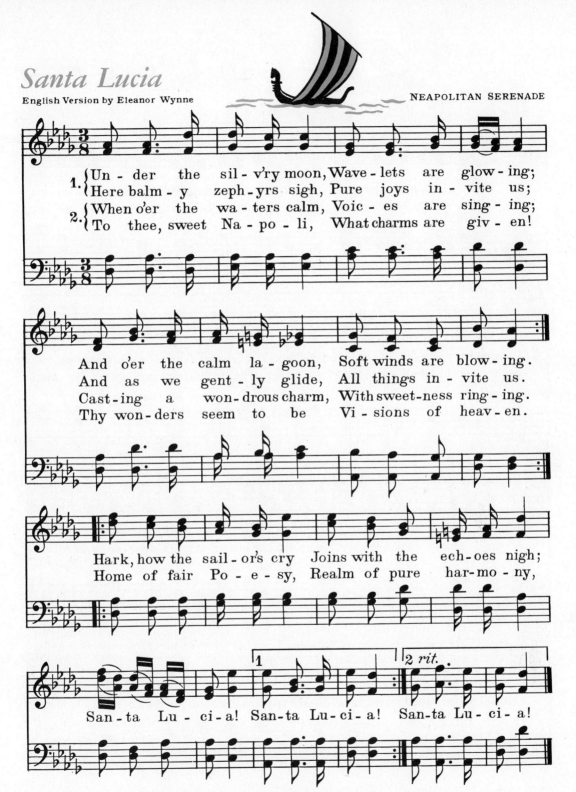

1. Un - der the sil - v'ry moon, Wave - lets are glow - ing;
   Here balm - y zeph - yrs sigh, Pure joys in - vite us;
2. When o'er the wa - ters calm, Voic - es are sing - ing;
   To thee, sweet Na - po - li, What charms are giv - en!

And o'er the calm la - goon, Soft winds are blow - ing.
And as we gent - ly glide, All things in - vite us.
Cast - ing a won - drous charm, With sweet - ness ring - ing.
Thy won - ders seem to be Vi - sions of heav - en.

Hark, how the sail - or's cry Joins with the ech - oes nigh;
Home of fair Po - e - sy, Realm of pure har - mo - ny,

San - ta Lu - ci - a! San - ta Lu - ci - a! San - ta Lu - ci - a!

Home, Sweet Home

JOHN HOWARD PAYNE

HENRY R. BISHOP

LISTEN   SING

1. 'Mid pleas-ures and pal - a - ces though we may roam, Be it ev - er so
2. An ex - ile from home, splen-dor daz-zles in vain; Oh, give me my

LISTEN

hum-ble, there's no place like home! A charm from the skies seems to
low - ly thatched cot - tage a - gain! The birds sing-ing gai - ly that

SING

hal - low us there, Which, seek thro' the world, is ne'er met with else-where.
come at my call; Give me them, with the peace of mind, dear - er than all.

CHORUS

LISTEN   SING

Home! home! sweet, sweet home! There's no place like home, there's no place like home.

Note : May be sung as two-part song (soprano and alto)

Sweet and Low

ALFRED TENNYSON

J. BARNBY

Larghetto   With gentle, rocking movement

1. Sweet and low, sweet and low, Wind of the west - ern sea; Low, low,
2. Sleep and rest, sleep and rest, Fa - ther will come to thee soon; Rest, rest, on

breathe and blow, Wind of the west - ern sea; O - ver the roll - ing
A. O - ver the
moth - er's breast, Fa - ther will come to thee soon, Fa - ther will come to his
A. Fa - ther will

wa - ters go, Come from the dy - ing moon and blow, Blow him a - gain to
wa - ters go, *A. B.* Come from the moon and blow,
babe in the nest, Sil - ver sails all out of the west, Un - der the sil - ver
come to his babe, *A. B.* Sil - ver sails out of the west,

me, While my lit - tle one, while my pret - ty one sleeps.
moon Sleep, my lit - tle one, sleep, my pret - ty one sleep.

185

Love's Old Sweet Song

G. CLIFTON BINGHAM

JAMES L. MOLLOY

Cantabile

1. Once in the dear, dead days be-yond re-call, When on the world the
2. E - ven to-day we hear love's song of yore, Deep in our hearts it

mists be-gan to fall, Out of the dreams that rose in hap - py throng,
dwells for - ev - er-more, Foot-steps may fal - ter, wea - ry grow the way,

Low to our hearts love sang an old sweet song, And in the dusk where
Still we can hear it at the close of day; So till the end when

rit.

fell the fire-light gleam, Soft - ly it wove it-self in - to our dream.
life's dim shad-ows fall, Love will be found the sweet-est song of all.

CHORUS *p* *Slightly faster*

Just a song at twi-light, when the lights are low, And the flick-'ring

poco rit. *a tempo*

shad-ows soft-ly come and go; Tho' the heart be wea-ry, sad the day and long,

rit. *pp*

Still to us at twi-light comes love's old song, Comes love's old sweet song.

Thanksgiving Prayer
(2105A)

ANONYMOUS

NETHERLANDS TUNE
Acc. by I. W.

In joyful praise

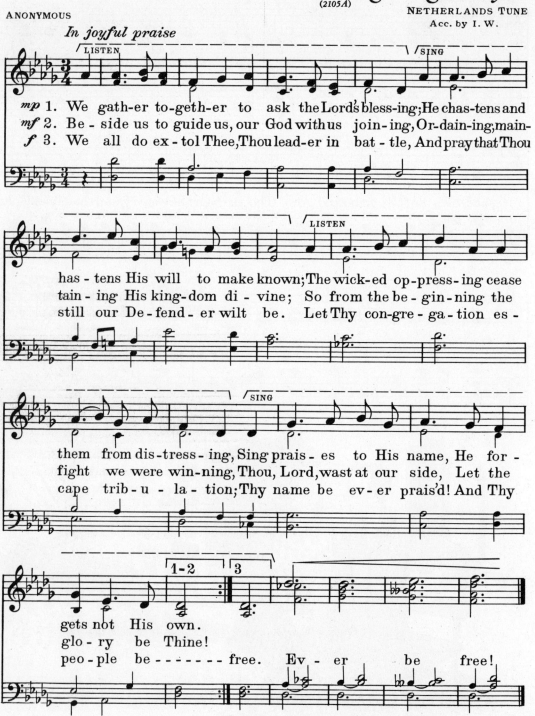

mp 1. We gath-er to-geth-er to ask the Lord's bless-ing; He chas-tens and
mf 2. Be - side us to guide us, our God with us join-ing, Or-dain-ing, main-
f 3. We all do ex - tol Thee, Thou lead-er in bat - tle, And pray that Thou

has - tens His will to make known; The wick-ed op-press-ing cease
tain - ing His king-dom di - vine; So from the be - gin-ning the
still our De - fend - er wilt be. Let Thy con-gre - ga-tion es -

them from dis-tress-ing, Sing prais-es to His name, He for -
fight we were win-ning, Thou, Lord, wast at our side, Let the
cape trib-u - la-tion; Thy name be ev-er prais'd! And Thy

gets not His own.
glo - ry be Thine!
peo-ple be - - - - - free. Ev - er be free!

Vale of Avoca

THOMAS MOORE

GERMAN FOLK SONG
Arr. by I.W.

With smooth, flowing phrases

1. There's not in the wide world A valley so sweet
2. Sweet vale of A-vo-ca! How calm could I rest
3. There storms that we feel in This cold world should cease,

As thine in whose sweet bos-om The bright wa-ters meet.
By thy sweet shad-owed stream-lets,O vale I love the best!
And our hearts like thy wa-ters Be min-gled there in peace,

As thine in whose sweet bos-om The bright wa-ters meet.
By thy sweet shad-owed stream-lets, O vale I love the best!
And our hearts like thy wa-ters Be min-gled there in peace.

TWO THEMES FROM DVORAK

Dvorak, the great Bohemian composer, lived for three years in America. While here he wrote the "New World" Symphony which tells us his impressions of our coun-try. This symphony was completed while Dvorak spent the summer in the Bohemian settlement in Spillville, Iowa.

The beautiful theme from the slow movement—*Largo*—suggests a Negro folk tune:

Dvorak also wrote many shorter pieces. One of the best known is his "Humoresque," first written for piano.

189

My Old Kentucky Home
(104B)

STEPHEN FOSTER

STEPHEN FOSTER

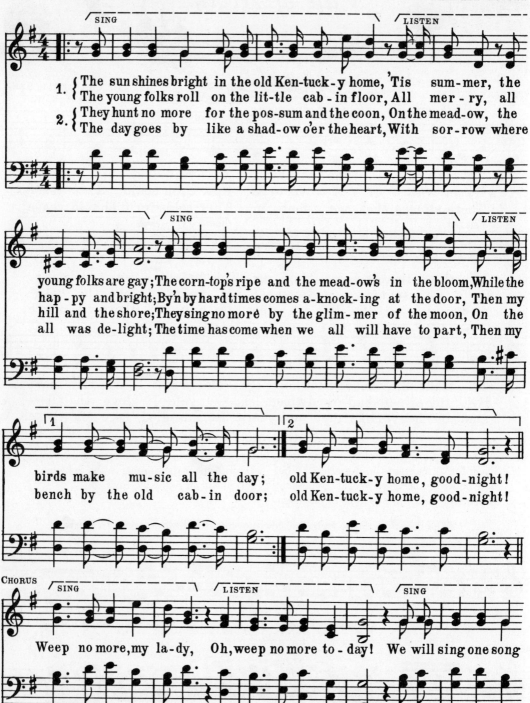

1. { The sun shines bright in the old Ken-tuck-y home, 'Tis sum-mer, the
   { The young folks roll on the lit-tle cab-in floor, All mer-ry, all
2. { They hunt no more for the pos-sum and the coon, On the mead-ow, the
   { The day goes by like a shad-ow o'er the heart, With sor-row where

young folks are gay; The corn-top's ripe and the mead-ow's in the bloom, While the
hap-py and bright; By'n by hard times comes a-knock-ing at the door, Then my
hill and the shore; They sing no more by the glim-mer of the moon, On the
all was de-light; The time has come when we all will have to part, Then my

birds make mu-sic all the day; old Ken-tuck-y home, good-night!
bench by the old cab-in door; old Ken-tuck-y home, good-night!

CHORUS

Weep no more, my la-dy, Oh, weep no more to-day! We will sing one song

for the old Ken-tuck-y home, For the old Ken-tuck-y home, far a-way.

Old Folks at Home
(2204B)

STEPHEN FOSTER   STEPHEN FOSTER

1. { 'Way down up-on the Swa-nee Riv-er, Far, far a-way,
     { All up and down the whole cre-a-tion, Sad-ly I roam,

2. { All round the lit-tle farm I wan-dered, When I was young;
     { When I was play-ing with my broth-er, Hap-py was I;

3. { One lit-tle hut a-mong the bush-es, One that I love,
     { When will I see the bees a-hum-ming All round the comb?

There's where my heart is turn-ing ev-er, There's where the old folks stay.
Still long-ing for the old plan-ta-tion, And for the old folks at home.
Then man-y hap-py days I squan-der'd, Man-y the songs I sung.
Oh! take me to my kind old moth-er, There let me live and die.
Still sad-ly to my mem-'ry rush-es, No mat-ter where I rove.
When will I hear the ban-jo tum-ming, Down in my good old home?

D. S. Oh! broth-ers, how my heart grows wea-ry, Far from the old folks at home.

REFRAIN

All the world is sad and drear-y, Ev-'ry where I roam;

191

Birthday of a King

(2001A)

W. H. NEIDLINGER

mp /SING

1. In the lit-tle vil-lage of Beth-le-hem, There lay a child one day,
2. 'Twas a hum-ble birth-place, but Oh, how much God gave to us that day!

/LISTEN

And the sky was bright with a ho-ly light O'er the place where Je-sus lay.
From the man-ger bed what a path hath led; What a per-fect ho-ly way.

mf /SING

Al-le-lu-ia! O how the an-gels sang, Al-le-lu-ia! how it rang!

f /LISTEN *rall.*

And the sky was bright with a ho-ly light: 'Twas the birth-day of a King!

The Holly and the Ivy

(203B) (2001B) ENGLISH TRADITIONAL CAROL

Cheerfully and like a dance

mf / —LISTEN /SING

1. The Hol-ly and the I-vy, When they are both full grown, Of___
2. The Hol-ly bears a prick-le As sharp as an-y thorn, And___
3. The Hol-ly bears a ber-ry As red as an-y blood, And___

/LISTEN

all the trees that are in the wood The Hol-ly bears the___ crown;
Mar-y bore sweet Je-sus Christ, On Christ-mas day in the morn; } Oh the
Mar-y bore sweet Je-sus Christ, To do poor sin-ners___ good; }

f /SING

ris-ing of the Sun,___ And the run-ning of the Deer, The

mp

play-ing of the mer-ry Or-gan, Sweet sing-ing in the Choir.

192

Sweetly Sleeping in the Manger

(2004B)

POLISH CAROL
Arr. by I. W.

With quiet joy

1. Sweet-ly sleep-ing in the man-ger, Lit-tle Je-sus, Ho-ly Child; Love is guard-ing gen-tle Jo-seph, Ho-ly Babe and Moth-er mild. All a-round good shep-herds low-ly, While a-bove in cho-rus ho-ly An-gels sing un-to our Lord.

2. Come we chil-dren to the man-ger, Look with love up-on the Child; Watch Him sleep-ing in the man-ger, Watch with Mar-y, Moth-er mild. Wor-ship we with shep-herds low-ly, Sing our praise with cho-rus ho-ly, Sing with joy un-to our Lord!

Christmas Hymn

KATE FORMAN

M. PRAETORIUS

Moderato

1. Ring out, sweet bells of Christ-mas, A-cross the mead-ows white; In
2. Ring out, sweet bells of Christ-mas, A-long the fields of snow, And
3. Ring out, sweet bells of Christ-mas, A-bove the frost-y hill; We

God is all the glo-ry, We see it day and night, We see it day and
tell us peace is com-ing To all the earth be-low, To all the earth be-
all are God's own chil-dren, And on-ly know good-will, And on-ly know good-

night. Ring out, sweet bells of Christ-mas, And tell us God is light.
low. Ring out, sweet bells of Christ-mas, Your peace can nev-er go.
will. Ring out, sweet bells of Christ-mas, Your song is nev-er still.

Hark! The Herald Angels Sing
(304A)   (2001A)

CHARLES WESLEY

MENDELSSOHN

Joyfully, with marching pulse

1. Hark! the her-ald an-gels sing, Glo-ry to the new-born King;
2. Gra-cious bond of earth and sky, Born that man no more may die,

Peace on earth, and mer-cy mild, God and sin-ners re-con-ciled.
Born to raise the sons of earth, Born to give them sec-ond birth.

Joy-ful, all ye na-tions, rise, Join the tri-umph of the skies;
Hail the heav'n born Prince of Peace! Hail the Sun of Right-eous-ness!

With th'an-gel-ic hosts pro-claim, Christ is born in Beth-le-hem!
Light and life to all He brings, Ris'n with heal-ing in His wings.

Hark! the her-ald an-gels sing, Glo-ry to the new-born King!
Hark! the her-ald an-gels sing, Glo-ry to the new-born King!

Deck the Halls with Boughs of Holly

(2001B)

OLD WELSH AIR

Cheerfully

mf

LISTEN — SING

1. Deck the halls with boughs of hol - ly, Fa la la la la la la la la.
2. See the blaz-ing Yule be-fore us, Fa la la la la la la la la.
3. Fast a-way the old year pass-es, Fa la la la la la la la la.

LISTEN — SING

'Tis the sea-son to be jol - ly, Fa la la la la la la la la.
Strike the harp and join the cho-rus, Fa la la la la la la la la.
Hail the new, ye lads and lass-es, Fa la la la la la la la la.

LISTEN — SING

Don we now our gay ap-par-el, Fa la la la la la la la la.
Fol-low me in mer-ry meas-ure, Fa la la la la la la la la.
Sing we joy-ous all to-geth-er, Fa la la la la la la la la.

LISTEN — SING

Troll the an-cient Yule-tide car-ol, Fa la la la la la la la la.
While I tell of Yule-tide treas-ure, Fa la la la la la la la la.
Heed-less of the wind and weath-er, Fa la la la la la la la la.

O Little Town of Bethlehem

PHILLIPS BROOKS   (2002A)   LEWIS H. REDNER

Peacefully

1. O lit - tle town of Beth-le-hem, How still we see thee lie! A -
bove thy deep and dream-less sleep The si - lent stars go by; Yet
in thy dark streets shin-eth The ev - er - last - ing Light; The
hopes and fears of all the years Are met in thee to - night.

2. For Christ is born of Mar - y; And gath-er'd all a - bove, While
mor-tals sleep, the an - gels keep Their watch of won-d'ring love. O
morn-ing stars, to - geth - er Pro-claim the ho - ly birth, And
prais - es sing to God the King, And peace to men on earth.

3. How si - lent-ly, how si - lent-ly, The won-drous gift is giv'n! So
God im-parts to hu - man hearts The bless-ings of His Heav'n. No
ear may hear His com - ing, But in this world of sin, Where
meek souls will re-ceive Him still, The dear Christ en - ters in.

4. O ho - ly Child of Beth-le-hem, De-scend to us we pray; Cast
out our sin and en - ter in, Be born in us to - day. We
hear the Christ-mas an - gels The great glad ti - dings tell; O
come to us, a - bide with us, Our Lord, Em-man - u - el.

Christmas Caroling Song
(104B) (2002B)
TRADITIONAL ENGLISH

In marching rhythm two steps per measure throughout

1. Here we come a - car-ol-ing A - mong the leaves so green;
2. We are not dai - ly beg - gars, That beg from door to door, But
3. God bless the Mas-ter of this house, Like-wise the Mis - tress, too; And

Here we come a - car-ol-ing So fair to be seen.
we are neigh-bors, chil - dren Whom you have seen be - fore.
all the lit - tle chil - dren That 'round the ta - ble go.

Love and joy come to you, And to you glad Christ-mas, too; And God bless you and

send you a Hap - py New Year, And God send you a Hap-py New Year.

The First Noel
(2005B)
TRADITIONAL   TRADITIONAL

mf

1. The first No - el the an-gels did say Was to cer-tain poor shep-herds in fields as they lay:
2. They look-ed up and saw a star Shin-ing in the East be - yond them far,
3. This star drew nigh to the north-west, O'er Beth - le - hem it took its rest,
4. Then en - ter'd in there Wise-men three, Full rev - 'rent-ly up - on their knee,

In fields where they lay keep-ing their sheep On a cold win-ter's night that was so deep.
And to the earth it gave great light, And so it con-tin-ued both day and night.
And there it did both stop and stay Right o-ver the place where Je - sus lay.
And of - fer'd there in His pres-ence, Their gold and myrrh and frank-in-cense.

CHORUS

ff

No - el, No - el, No - el, No - el,— Born is the King of Is - ra - el.

Silent Night

JOSEPH MOHR   *(104A)*   *(2005A)*   FRANZ GRUBER

p LISTEN   *pp* SING   *mf* LISTEN   *p* SING

1. Si - lent night! Ho - ly night! All is calm, all is bright!
2. Si - lent night! Ho - ly night! Shep-herds quake at the sight!
3. Si - lent night! Ho - ly night! Son of God, love's pure light,

LISTEN   *poco cresc.* SING

'Round yon vir - gin moth-er and Child! Ho - ly In-fant, so ten-der and mild,
Glo - ries stream from heav-en a - far, Heav'n-ly hosts sing Al - le - lu - ia,
Ra - diant, beams from Thy ho - ly face With the dawn of re - deem - ing grace,

pp LISTEN   *p* SING

Sleep in heav - en - ly peace,   Sleep in heav - en - ly peace.
Christ, the Sav - iour, is born,   Christ, the Sav - iour, is born.
Je - sus, Lord, at Thy birth,   Je - sus, Lord, at Thy birth.

Note: May be sung as two-part song (soprano and alto)

Good King Wenceslas

(2004A)

TRADITIONAL
Harmonized by Sir John Stainer

1. Good King Wen - ces - las look'd out, On the Feast of Ste - phen,
2. "Hith - er, page, and stand by me, If thou know'st it tell - ing,
3. "Bring me flesh and bring me wine, Bring me pine logs hith - er;
4. "Sire, the night is dark - er now, And the wind blows strong - er;
5. In his mas - ter's steps he trod, Where the snow lay dint - ed;

When the snow lay round a - bout, Deep and crisp and e - ven.
Yon - der peas - ant, who is he? Where and what his dwell - ing?"
Thou and I will see him dine, When we bear them thith - er."
Fails my heart, I know not how, I can go no long - er."
Heat was in the ver - y sod Which the Saint had print - ed.

Bright - ly shone the moon that night, Though the frost was cru - el,
"Sire, he lives a good league hence, Un - der - neath the moun - tain;
Page and mon - arch forth they went, Forth they went to - geth - er;
"Mark my foot-steps, my good page, Tread thou in them bold - ly;
There-fore, Chris - tian men, be sure, Wealth or rank pos - sess - ing,

When a poor man came in sight, Gath'ring win - ter fu - el.
Right a-gainst the for - est fence, By Saint Ag - nes' foun - tain."
Thro' the rough winds' wild la - ment And the bit - ter weath - er.
Thou shalt find the win-ter's rage Freeze thy blood less cold - ly."
Ye who now will bless the poor, Shall your-selves find bless - ing.

Hymn for the Nations

(2102A)

JOSEPHINE DASKAM BACON

LUDWIG VAN BEETHOVEN
from the Ninth Symphony

With spirit

LISTEN

1. Broth-er, sing your coun-try's an - them, Shout your land's un - dy - ing fame;
2. Hail the sun of peace, new ris - ing, Hold the war clouds clos-er furled.
3. Build the road of Peace be-fore us, Build it wide and deep and long:

SING

Light the won-drous tale of na-tions With your peo-ple's gold-en name.
Blend our ban-ners, O my broth-er, In the rain-bow of the world!
Speed the slow and check the ea-ger, Help the weak and curb the strong.

LISTEN

Tell your fa-thers' no-ble sto-ry, Raise on high your coun-try's sign,
Red as blood, and blue as heav-en, Wise as age, and proud as youth,
None shall push a - side an-oth-er, None shall let an - oth - er fall:

SING

Join, then, in the fi - nal glo - ry-Broth-er, lift your flag with mine!
Melt our col-ors, won-der wov-en, In the great white light of Truth!
March be-side me, O my broth-er, All for one, and one for all!

This poem was awarded the first prize in a nation-wide contest of Ameri-can poets, sponsored by the League of Nations Association, Inc., for the best international hymn.

All Glory, Laud, and Honor

ST. THEODULPH, c.820
Tr. by John Mason Neale, 1866

MELCHIOR TESCHNER, 1635

REFRAIN★ *Majestically*

/LISTEN

All glo-ry, laud, and hon-or, To Thee, Re-deem-er, King!

/SING .... *Fine*

To Whom the lips of chil-dren Made sweet ho-san-nas ring.

/LISTEN

1. Thou art the King of Is-rael, Thou Da-vid's roy-al Son,
2. The com-pa-ny of an-gels Are prais-ing Thee on high,
3. The peo-ple of the He-brews With palms be-fore Thee went;
4. To Thee be-fore Thy pas-sion They sang their hymns of praise;
5. Thou didst ac-cept their prais-es; Ac-cept the praise we bring,

/SING .... ⌐D.C.

Who in the Lord's name com-est, The King and Bless-ed One!
And mor-tal men and all things Cre-a-ted make re-ply.
Our praise and prayers and an-thems Be-fore Thee we pre-sent.
To Thee, now high ex-alt-ed, Our mel-o-dy we raise.
Who in all good de-light-est, Thou good and gra-cious King.

★ Refrain to be sung before each stanza and at the close. Song may be sung in unison, in two parts for soprano and alto voices, or in four parts.

All Things Bright and Beautiful
(203A)

CECIL FRANCIS ALEXANDER

Traditional English Melody
Arr. by I.W.

REFRAIN★ *With joyful spirit*

All things bright and beau-ti-ful, All crea-tures great and small,

All things wise and won-der-ful, The Lord God made them all.

1. Each lit-tle flower that o-pens, Each lit-tle bird that sings,
2. The pur-ple-head-ed moun-tain, The riv-er run-ning by,
3. The cold wind in the win-ter, The pleas-ant sum-mer sun,
4. The tall trees in the green-wood, The mead-ows where we play,
5. He gave us eyes to see them, And lips that we might tell

He made their glow-ing col-ors, He made their ti-ny wings.
The sun-set, and the morn-ing That bright-ens up the sky.
The ripe fruits in the gar-den, He made them ev-'ry one.
The rush-es by the wa-ter We gath-er ev-'ry day.
How great is God Al-might-y, Who has made all things well.

★ Refrain to be sung first, and after each stanza. During stanza altos and baritones hum their parts while sopranos sing the words.

Oh Come, All Ye Faithful (Adeste Fideles)

(2004A)

Tr. from the Latin
by Frederick Oakley

JOHN READING

1. Oh come, all ye faith-ful, Joy-ful and tri-um-phant, Oh come ye, oh come ye to Beth-le-hem; Come and be-hold Him, Born the King of an-gels;
2. Sing, choirs of an-gels, Sing in ex-ul-ta-tion; Sing, all ye cit-i-zens of heav'n a-bove: Glo-ry to God In the high-est;
3. Yea, Lord, we greet Thee, Born this hap-py morn-ing, Je-sus, to Thee be glo-ry giv'n; Word of the Fa-ther, Now in flesh ap-pear-ing;

Oh come, let us a-dore Him, Oh come, let us a-dore Him, Oh come, let us a-dore Him, Christ, the Lord. A-men.

Rejoice, Ye Pure in Heart

PLUMPTRE

MESSITER
Arr. by I. W.

With joyful vitality

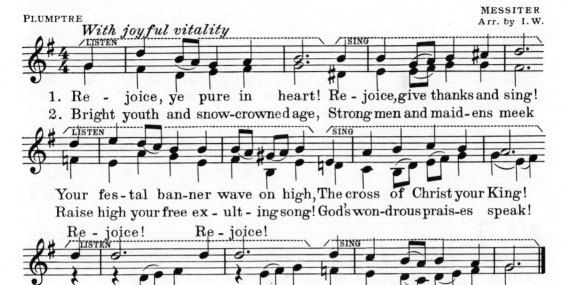

1. Re - joice, ye pure in heart! Re-joice, give thanks and sing!
2. Bright youth and snow-crowned age, Strong men and maid-ens meek

Your fes-tal ban-ner wave on high, The cross of Christ your King!
Raise high your free ex - ult - ing song! God's won-drous prais-es speak!

Re - joice! Re - joice!

Re - joice! Re - joice! Re-joice, give thanks and sing!

AN ORATORIO—BIBLE TEXTS SET TO MUSIC

Handel wrote some of the world's greatest religious music. This beautiful
contralto solo is from the oratorio, "The Messiah," which was his most in-
spired work. The radio brings it to us each year at Christmas time.

He Shall Feed His Flock

HANDEL

He_ shall feed his flock like a shep_____ herd, And He_ shall_gath-er

This Is My Father's World

(203B)

MALTBIE D. BABCOCK

TRADITIONAL ENGLISH MELODY
Arr. by Franklin L. Sheppard

1. This is my Fa-ther's world, And to my lis-tening ears, All na-ture sings, and round me rings The mu-sic of the spheres. This is my Fa-ther's world, I rest me in the thought Of rocks and trees, of skies and seas His hand the won-ders wrought.

2. This is my Fa-ther's world, The birds their car-ols raise, The morn-ing light, the lil-y white, De-clare their Mak-er's praise. This is my Fa-ther's world, He shines in all that's fair; In the rus-tling grass I hear him pass, He speaks to me ev-'ry-where.

3. This is my Fa-ther's world, O let me ne'er for-get That tho' the wrong seems oft so strong, God is the Rul-er yet. This is my Fa-ther's world, Why should my heart be sad? The Lord is King, let the heav-ens ring: God reigns: let the earth be glad. A-men.

For the Beauty of the Earth

FOLLIOT S. PIERPONT

Arr. from Conrad Kocher

Moderato

1. For the beau-ty of the earth, For the beau-ty of the skies,
2. For the beau-ty of each hour Of the day and of the night,
3. For the joy of hu-man love, Broth-er, sis-ter, par-ent, child,
4. For each per-fect gift of Thine To our race so free-ly giv'n,

For the love which from our birth O - ver and a-round us lies,
Hill and vale, and tree and flow'r, Sun and moon, and stars of light,
Friends on earth and friends a-bove, For all gen-tle thoughts and mild,
Grac-es, hu-man and di-vine, Flow'rs of earth and buds of heav'n,

Lord of all, to Thee we raise This our hymn of grate-ful praise.

We Would Be Building

PURD E. DIETZ

JEAN SIBELIUS
(Finlandia)

Sustained, with majestic phrase line

1. We would be build-ing; tem-ples still un-done____ O'er crum-bling
2. Teach us to build; up-on the sol-id rock____ We set the
3. O keep us build-ing, Mas-ter; may our hands____ Ne'er fal-ter

walls their cross-es scarce-ly lift;__Wait-ing till love can raise the bro-ken
dream that hard-ens in-to deed,__Ribbed with the steel that time and change doth
when the dream is in our hearts,__When to our ears there come di-vine com-

stone,__And hearts cre-a-tive bridge the hu-man rift;__We would be
mock,__Th'un fail-ing pur-pose of our no-blest creed;__Teach us to
mands__And all the pride of sin-ful will de-parts;__We build with

build-ing, Mas-ter, let Thy plan__Re-veal the life that God would give to man.
build, O Mas-ter, lend us sight__To see the tow-ers gleam-ing in the light.
Thee, O grant en-dur-ing worth__Un-til the heav'n-ly King-dom comes on earth.

America, the Beautiful

KATHARINE LEE BATES (2103B)

SAMUEL A. WARD

mf Majestically, with clean rhythm

Same rhythm in all 4 phrases

1. O beau-ti-ful for spa-cious skies, For am-ber waves of grain, For pur-ple moun-tain maj-es-ties A-bove the fruit-ed plain. A-mer-i-ca! A-mer-i-ca! God shed His grace on thee, And crown thy good with broth-er-hood From sea to shin-ing sea.

2. O beau-ti-ful for pil-grim feet Whose stern im-pas-sioned stress, A thor-ough-fare for free-dom beat A-cross the wil-der-ness. A-mer-i-ca! A-mer-i-ca! God mend thine ev-'ry flaw, Con-firm thy soul in self-con-trol, Thy lib-er-ty in law.

3. O beau-ti-ful for he-roes prov'd In lib-er-at-ing strife, Who more than self their coun-try loved, And mer-cy more than life. A-mer-i-ca! A-mer-i-ca! May God thy gold re-fine Till all suc-cess be no-ble-ness And ev-'ry gain di-vine.

4. O beau-ti-ful for pa-triot dreams That sees be-yond the years Thine al-a-bas-ter cit-ies gleam, Un-dimmed by hu-man tears. A-mer-i-ca! A-mer-i-ca! God shed His grace on thee, And crown thy good with broth-er-hood From sea to shin-ing sea.

Battle Hymn of the Republic

(2104B)

JULIA WARD HOWE

Old Tune: John Brown's Body

SING

1. Mine eyes have seen the glo-ry of the com-ing of the Lord;
2. He has sound-ed forth the trum-pet that shall nev-er call re-treat;
3. In the beau-ty of the lil-ies Christ was born a-cross the sea,

LISTEN

He is tramp-ling out the vin-tage where the grapes of wrath are stored;
He is sift-ing out the hearts of men be-fore His judg-ment seat.
With a glo-ry in His bos-om that trans-fig-ures you and me;

SING

He hath loosed the fate-ful light-'ning of his ter-ri-ble swift sword;
Oh, be swift, my soul, to an-swer Him! be ju-bi-lant, my feet,
As He died to make men ho-ly let us die to make men free,

LISTEN   CHORUS SING

His truth is march-ing on.   His
Our God is march-ing on.   Glo-ry, glo-ry, hal-le-lu-jah!
While God is march-ing on.

Glo-ry, glo-ry, hal-le-lu-jah! truth is march-ing on.

America
(2101B)

SAMUEL F. SMITH   HENRY CAREY

1. My coun-try 'tis of thee, Sweet land of lib-er-ty,
2. My na-tive coun-try, thee, Land of the no-ble free,
3. Let mu-sic swell the breeze, And ring from all the trees,
4. Our fa-thers' God, to Thee, Au-thor of lib-er-ty,

Of thee I sing! Land where my fa-thers died, Land of the
Thy name I love; I love thy rocks and rills, Thy woods and
Sweet free-dom's song; Let mor-tal tongues a-wake, Let all that
To Thee we sing! Long may our land be bright With free-dom's

pil-grim's pride; From ev-'ry moun-tain side Let free-dom ring!
tem-pled hills; My heart with rap-ture thrills, Like that a-bove.
breathe par-take, Let rocks their si-lence break, The sound pro-long.
ho-ly light, Pro-tect us by Thy might, Great God, our King!

211

Dixie Land

DAN EMMETT

(2103A) DAN EMMETT
Arr. by Collin Coe

Lively

mp LISTEN

1. I wish I was in de land of cot-ton,
2. Dar's buck-wheat cakes an' In-gen bat-ter

SING *f*

Old times dar am not for-got-ten, Look a-way! Look a-way! Look a-
Makes you fat or a lit-tle fat-ter, Look a-way! Look a-way! Look a-

LISTEN *mp*

way! Dix-ie Land. In Dix-ie Land whar I was born in, Ear-ly on one
way! Dix-ie Land. Den hoe it down an' scratch your grab-ble, To Dix-ie land I'm

frosty mornin', Look a-way! Look a-way! Look a-way! Dix-ie Land.
bound to trab-ble, Look a-way! Look a-way! Look a-way! Dix-ie Land.

CHORUS

Den I wish I was in Dix-ie, Hoo-ray! Hoo-ray! In Dix-ie Land I'll

take my stand, To lib and die in Dix-ie, A-way, A-way, A-

way down south in Dix-ie, A-way, A-way, A-way down south in Dix-ie.

The Star-Spangled Banner

FRANCIS SCOTT KEY (d. 1843)

(2101A)

STAFFORD SMITH

The Marines' Hymn
(2105B)

March tempo

/LISTEN

1. From the Halls of Mon-te-zu-ma   To the shores of Trip-o-li,
2. Our   flag's un-furled to ev-'ry breeze From dawn to set-ting sun;
3. Here's   health to you and to our corps Which we are proud to serve;

/SING

We   fight our coun-try's bat - tles On the land as on the sea.
We have fought in ev-'ry clime and place Where we could take a gun.
In   man-y a strife we've fought for life And nev-er lost our nerve.

/LISTEN

First to fight for right and free - dom And to keep our hon-or clean;
In the snow of far off North-ern lands And in sun-ny trop-ic scenes;
If the Ar-my and the Na-vy Ev-er look on Heav-en's scenes,

/SING

We are proud to claim the ti - tle Of U-nit-ed States Ma-rines.
You will find us al-ways on the job The U-nit-ed States Ma-rines.
They will find the streets are guard - ed By U-nit-ed States Ma-rines.

Reveille

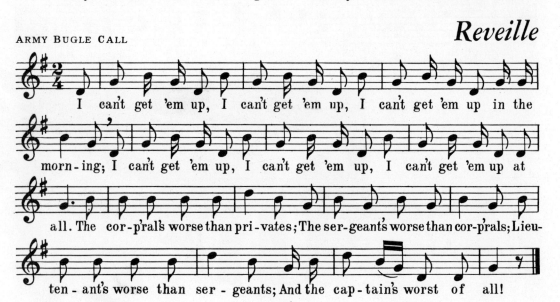

I can't get 'em up, I can't get 'em up, I can't get 'em up in the
morn-ing; I can't get 'em up, I can't get 'em up, I can't get 'em up at
all. The cor-p'ral's worse than pri-vates; The ser-geant's worse than cor-p'rals; Lieu-
ten-ant's worse than ser-geants; And the cap-tain's worst of all!

216

Caissons Go Rolling Along
(2102B)

U.S. FIELD ARTILLERY SONG

Words & Music by
EDMUND L. GRUBER

With two quick steps per measure

O-ver hill, o-ver dale, we have hit the dust-y trail And those cais-sons go rolling a - long. ___ In and out hear them shout "Count-er march and right a - bout" And those cais-sons go roll-ing a - long. ___ Then it's Hi! Hi! Hee! in the Field Ar-til-ler - y, Sound off your num-bers loud and strong ___ Where e'er you go you will al-ways know That those cais-sons are rolling a - long (Keep them roll-ing) And those cais-sons go roll-ing a - long. ___

Taps

ARMY BUGLE CALL

Day is done, Gone the sun, From the lake, From the hill, From the sky, All is well, Safe - ly rest, God is nigh!

When Johnny Comes Marching Home

(2105A)

LOUIS LAMBERT
With jubilant spirit

LOUIS LAMBERT
Arr. by I.W.

LISTEN

1. When John-ny comes march-ing home a-gain, Hur - rah, Hur - rah!
2. The old-church bell will peal with joy, Hur - rah, Hur - rah!
3. Get read - y for the Ju - bi - lee, Hur - rah, Hur - rah!

SING

LISTEN

We'll give him a heart - y wel-come then, Hur - rah, Hur - rah!
To wel - come home our dar-ling boy, Hur - rah, Hur - rah!
We'll give— the he - ro three times three, Hur - rah, Hur - rah!

SING

LISTEN

The men will cheer, the boys will shout, The la-dies, they will all turn out,
The vil-lage lads and las-sies gay, With ros - es they will strew the way,
The lau-rel wreath is read-y now To place up-on his loy-al brow,

SING

And we'll all feel gay, When John-ny comes march-ing home!
And we'll all feel gay, When John-ny comes march-ing home!
And we'll all feel gay, When John-ny comes march-ing home!

Yankee Doodle

(2103A)

R. SHACKBURG

AMERICAN COLONIAL SONG

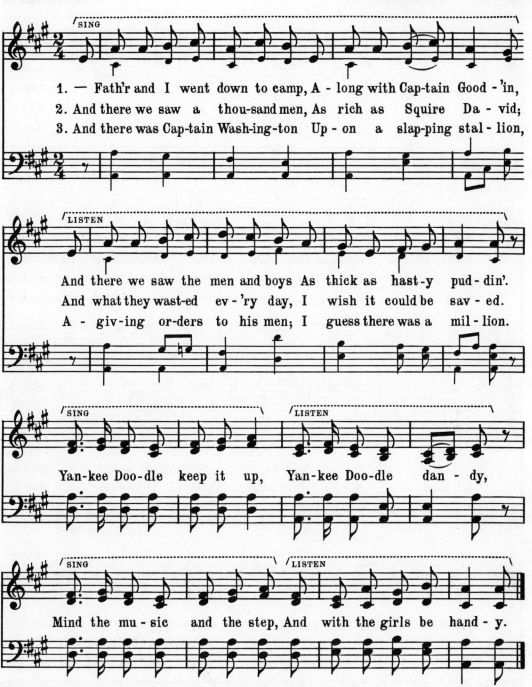

1. — Fath'r and I went down to camp, A-long with Cap-tain Good-'in,
2. And there we saw a thou-sand men, As rich as Squire Da-vid;
3. And there was Cap-tain Wash-ing-ton Up-on a slap-ping stal-lion,

And there we saw the men and boys As thick as hast-y pud-din'.
And what they wast-ed ev-'ry day, I wish it could be sav-ed.
A-giv-ing or-ders to his men; I guess there was a mil-lion.

Yan-kee Doo-dle keep it up, Yan-kee Doo-dle dan-dy,

Mind the mu-sic and the step, And with the girls be hand-y.

May be sung in unison or by a solo voice to the refrain, then soprano-alto duet or full harmony.

Columbia, the Gem of the Ocean

(2104A)

THOMAS A'BECKET

ORIGIN UNCERTAIN

Majestically

1. O Co - lum - bia, the gem of the o - cean, The
2. When war wing'd its wide des - o - la - tion, And
3. The star span-gled ban - ner bring hith - er, O'er Co-

home of the brave and the free, The shrine of each pa-triot's de-
threat-end the land to de - form, The ark then of free-dom's foun-
lum-bia's true sons let it wave; May the wreaths they have won nev-er

vo-tion, A world of-fers hom-age to thee. Thy
da-tion, Co - lum-bia rode safe thru the storm, With her
with-er, Nor its stars cease to shine on the brave; May thy

man-dates make he - roes as - sem-ble, When Lib - er-ty's form stands in
gar-lands of vic-t'ry a - round her, When so proud-ly she bore her brave
ser-vice, u-nit - ed ne'er sev - er, But hold to their col-ors so

view;   Thy   ban-ners make tyr - an-ny trem-ble,   When
crew;   With her flag proud-ly   float-ing be - fore her,   The
true;   The   ar - my and   na - vy for - ev - er,   Three

DUET

borne by the red, white, and blue!   When borne by the red, white, and
boast of the red, white, and blue!   The boast of the red, white, and
cheers for the red, white, and blue!   Three cheers for the red, white, and

blue!   When borne by the red, white, and blue!   Thy
blue!   The   boast of the red, white, and blue!   With her
blue!   Three cheers for the red, white, and blue!   The

ban-ners make tyr-an-ny trem-ble,   When borne by the red, white, and blue!
flag proud-ly float-ing be - fore her,   The boast of the red, white, and blue!
ar - my and na - vy for - ev - er,   Three cheers for the red, white, and blue!

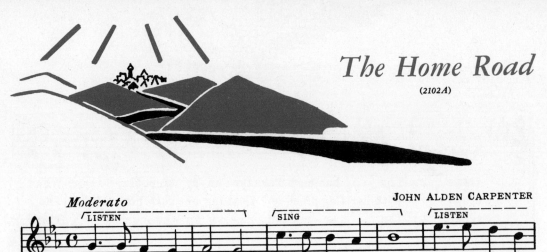

The Home Road
(2102A)

JOHN ALDEN CARPENTER

Moderato

LISTEN · SING · LISTEN

mf 1. Sing a hymn of free-dom, Fling the ban-ner high! Sing the songs of

mp 2. In the qui - et hours Of the star-ry night! Dream the dreams of

SING · LISTEN

Lib - er - ty, Songs that shall not die For the long, long road to Tip-pe-

far a - way, Home fires burn-ing bright

SING · LISTEN

ra - ry Is the road that leads me home, O'er hills and plains, By

God of Our Fathers

(2104B)

DANIEL C. ROBERTS

GEORGE W. WARREN

lakes and lanes, My Wood-lands! My Corn-fields! My Coun-try! My Home!

Trumpets or organ before each verse.

1. God of our fa-thers, whose al-might-y hand
2. Thy love di-vine hath led us in the past,
3. From war's a-larms, from dead-ly pes-ti-lence,
4. Re-fresh Thy peo-ple on their toil-some way,

Leads forth in beau-ty all the star-ry band   Of shin-ing worlds in
In this free land by Thee our lot is cast;   Be Thou our Rul-er,
Be Thy strong arm our ev-er sure de-fense;   Thy true re-lig-ion
Lead us from night to nev-er end-ing day;   Fill all our lives with

splen-dor thro' the skies,   Our grate-ful songs be-fore Thy throne a-rise.
Guard-ian, Guide and Stay,   Thy word our law, Thy paths our chos-en way.
in our hearts in-crease,   Thy boun-teous good-ness nour-ish us in peace.
love and grace di-vine,   And glo-ry, laud, and praise be ev-er Thine.

O Come, O Come, Immanuel

FROM THE LATIN, 12TH CENTURY

ANCIENT PLAIN SONG, 13TH CENTURY

IN UNISON

1. O come, O come, Im-man-u-el, And ran-som cap-tive
2. O come, Thou Wis-dom from on high, And or-der all things,
3. O come, De-sire of na-tions, bind All peo-ples in one

Is-ra-el, That mourns in lone-ly ex-ile here
far and nigh; To us the path of know-ledge show,
heart and mind; Bid en-vy, strife, and quar-rels cease;

HARMONY

Un-til the Son of God ap-pear. Re-joice! Re-joice! Im-
And cause us in her ways to go. Re-joice! Re-joice! Im-
Fill the whole world with heav-en's peace. Re-joice! Re-joice! Im-

man-u-el Shall come to thee, O Is-ra-el!
man-u-el Shall come to thee, O Is-ra-el!
man-u-el Shall come to thee, O Is-ra-el! A-men.

God Rest You Merry, Gentlemen

TRADITIONAL   (2002A)   ENGLISH CAROL

1. God rest you mer - ry, gen-tle-men, Let noth-ing you dis - may,
2. From God our Heav'n-ly Fa - ther, A bless-ed an - gel came,
3. And when they came to Beth-le-hem Where our dear Sav-iour lay,
4. Now to the Lord sing prais - es, All you with-in this place,

Re - mem-ber Christ our Sav - iour Was born on Christ-mas day,
And un - to cer - tain shep - herds Brought tid-ings of the same:
They found Him in a man - ger, Where ox - en feed on hay;
And with true love and broth-er-hood Each oth - er now em - brace;

To save us all from Sa-tan's pow'r, When we are gone a - stray;
How that in Beth-le - hem was born The Son of God by name.
His Moth-er Mar - y kneel-ing down, Un - to the Lord did pray.
This ho - ly tide of Christ-mas All oth - er doth de - face.

O — tid-ings of com-fort and joy, com-fort and joy, O — tid-ings of com-fort and joy!

★ Refrain arranged for boys' voices. If necessary, bass part may be omitted.

225

We Three Kings of Orient Are
(2002B)

JOHN H. HOPKINS

JOHN H. HOPKINS
Arr. by I.W.

Solo or Unison

Unison— 1. We three kings of O-ri-ent are, Bear-ing gifts we trav-erse a - far,
First King— 2. Born a King on Beth-le-hem's plain, Gold I bring to crown Him a - gain;
Second King— 3. Frank-in-cense to of-fer have I; In-cense owns a De - i - ty nigh,
Third King— 4. Myrrh is mine; its bit-ter per - fume Breathes a life of gath-'ring gloom;
Unison— 5. Glo-rious now be - hold Him rise, King and God and sac - ri - fice;

Field and foun-tain, moor and moun-tain, Fol-low-ing yon-der star.
King for - ev - er, ceas-ing nev - er, O - ver us all to reign.
Pray'r and prais-ing, all men rais-ing, Wor - ship God on high.
Sorr'w-ing, sigh-ing, bleed-ing, dy - ing, Sealed in the stone cold tomb.
Heav'n sings "Hal - le - lu - jah!" "Hal - le - lu - jah" earth re - plies.

REFRAIN   *With good movement*

Oh — star of won - der, star of night, Star with roy - al beau-ty bright,

West-ward lead-ing, still pro-ceed-ing, Guide us to the per-fect light.

★Refrain arranged for boys' voices in three-part harmony (treble staff).

Joy to the World
(2003B)

ISAAC WATTS

GEORGE F. HANDEL
Arr. by Lowell Mason

1. Joy to the world! The Lord is come; Let earth re - ceive her King;
2. Joy to the world! The Sav - iour reigns; Let men their songs em - ploy;
3. No more let sin and sor - row grow, Nor thorns in - fest the ground;
4. He rules the world with truth and grace, And makes the na - tions prove

Let ev - 'ry heart pre - pare Him room,
While fields and floods, rocks, hills, and plains,
He comes to make His bless - ings flow
The glo - ries of His right - eous - ness,

And heaven and na - ture sing, And heaven and na - ture
Re - peat the sound - ing joy, Re - peat the sound - ing
Far as the curse is found, Far as the curse is
And won - ders of His love, And won - ders of His

And heaven, And heaven and na - ture sing, And
Re - peat, Re - peat the sound - ing joy, Re -
Far as, Far as the curse is found Far
And won - ders, won - ders of His love, And

sing, And heaven, and heaven and na - ture sing.
joy, Re - peat, re - peat the sound - ing joy.
found, Far as, far as the curse is found.
love, And won - ders, won - ders of His love.

heaven and na - ture sing,
peat the sound - ing joy,
as the curse is found,
won - ders of His love,

Angels We Have Heard on High

(2002B)

OLD FRENCH CAROL

1. An-gels we have heard on high, Sweet-ly sing-ing o'er the plains;
2. Shep-herds, why this ju-bi-lee? Why your joy-ous strains pro-long?
3. Come to Beth-le-hem and see Him whose birth the an-gels sing;

And the moun-tains in re-ply Ech-o-ing their joy-ous strains.
What the glad-some tid-ings be Which in-spire your heav'n-ly song?
Come, a-dore on bend-ed knee Christ, the Lord, the new-born King.

In joyful praise

Glo - - - - - - - - ri - a

in ex-cel-sis De - o, in ex-cel-sis De - o!

Deo pronounced dā-ō.

The gloria should be sung with pure vowels and lovely tone; all voices in unison or divided between soprano and alto parts (full harmony if bass and tenor voices are available). It is more expressive if the intensity is varied, once loud, next time soft, or vice versa.

O Saviour Sweet

(2003B)

I.W., from the German

S. SCHEIDT, 1650
Harmonized by J.S. Bach

Reverently

1. O Sav - iour sweet, O Sav - iour mild, Who came to
2. O Sav - iour sweet, O Sav - iour mild, Look Thou with

earth a lit - tle child. As Mar - y kept Thee
love on ev - 'ry child; Thou came from Heav'n a -

safe in love, Do Thou watch o'er us from a - bove;
bove to fill The hearts of men with kind good - will;

O Lit - tle One sweet, O Je - sus mild.
O Sav - iour sweet, O Je - sus mild.

Rise Up, Shepherd, and Foller
(2205B)

NEGRO FOLK CAROL
Arr. by I.W.

There's a star in the East on Christ-mas morn, Rise up, shep-herd, and fol-ler!

fol - ler!

Lead where

It will lead to the place where the Sav-iour's born, Rise up, shep-herd, and fol-ler!

Lead where

Leave your sheep and leave your lambs, Rise up, shep-herd, and fol-ler!

Leave sheep, leave lambs, Leave your

Leave your ewes and leave your rams, Rise up, shep-herd, and fol-ler!

ewes and

Fol - ler, fol - ler! Rise up, shep-herd, and fol - ler!

fol-ler the

Fol-ler the star to Beth-le - hem, Rise up, shep-herd, and fol - ler!

star to

What You Goin' to Name Him?
(2004B)

Simply, unhurriedly

NEGRO CAROL
By John W. Work, Sr.

(ONE VOICE) O Mar - y, what you goin' to name that pret-ty lit-tle ba - by?

Quite slowly

(ALL VOICES) Glo - ry! Glo - ry! Glo - ry to that new-born King!

A little faster

(SECOND VOICE) Some call Him one thing, I think I'll call Him Je - sus.
(THIRD VOICE) Some call Him one thing, I think I'll say Im - man - uel.

Slowly

(ALL VOICES) Glo - ry! Glo - ry! Glo - ry to that new-born King!

By permission of Theo. Presser Co., from *American Negro Songs* by John W. Work

What Child Is This?

TRADITIONAL *E minor*

(2005A) OLD ENGLISH TUNE: "GREENSLEEVES"
Arranged by Sir John Stainer

1. What Child is this, Who, laid to rest On Mar-y's lap, is sleep-ing? Whom an-gels greet with an-thems sweet, While shep-herds watch are keep-ing?
2. Why lies He in such mean es-tate, Where ox and ass are feed-ing? Good Chris-tian, fear: for sin-ners here The si-lent Word is plead-ing:
3. So bring Him in-cense, gold, and myrrh, Come peas-ant, king, to own Him; The King of Kings sal-va-tion brings; Let lov-ing hearts en-throne Him.

REFRAIN

This, this is Christ the King, Whom shep-herds guard and an-gels sing; Haste, haste to bring Him laud, The Babe, the Son of Mar-y!
Nails, spear, shall pierce Him through, The Cross be borne, for me, for you; Hail, hail, the Word made flesh, The Babe, the Son of Mar-y!
Raise, raise the song on high, The Vir-gin sings her lul-la-by; Joy, joy, for Christ is born, The Babe, the Son of Mar-y!

232

It Came Upon the Midnight Clear

(2003B)

EDWIN H. SEARS

RICHARD S. WILLIS

With easy movement

1. It came up-on the mid-night clear, That glo-rious song of old,
2. Still thro' the clo-ven skies they come, With peace-ful wings un - furled;
3. For lo! the days are has-t'ning on, By proph-ets seen of old,

From an-gels bend-ing near the earth, To touch their harps of gold:
And still their heav'n-ly mu - sic floats O'er all the wea - ry world.
When with the ev - er cir-cling years Shall come the time fore - told,

"Peace on the earth, good-will to men From heav'n's all gra-cious King,"
A - bove its sad and low-ly plains They bend on hov'ring wing,
When the new heav'n and earth shall own The Prince of Peace their King,

The world in sol-emn still-ness lay To hear the an-gels sing.
And ev - er o'er its Ba-bel sounds The bless-ed an-gels sing.
And the whole world send back the song Which now the an-gels sing.

Pat-a-Pan

(2002B)

Translated from the
Old French by I.W.
(Flute Opt'l.)

BURGUNDIAN CAROL
Arr. by I.W.

Lightly, quickly

Voice

SING   LISTEN

1. Rob-in bring your flute and come, Bil-lie play your bright new drum,
2. E-vil thoughts are o-ver-come By the love of God through one
3. God and man are more at one Than the sound-ing fife and drum

SING   LISTEN

Sing and play a light ta-tum, Tu-re-lu-re-lu, Pat-a-pat-a-pan,
Come to earth, His Ho-ly Son, Tu-re-lu-re-lu, Pat-a-pat-a-pan,
When His love to us is come, Tu-re-lu-re-lu, Pat-a-pat-a-pan,

poco rit.

1-2   3

SING   LISTEN   LISTEN

Sing and play a light ta-tum, Christmas joy's for ev-'ry-one.
Thus our Christmas joy be-gan, Pre-cious gift from God to man.
So when Christmas time is come, We will sing and play ta-   tum.

234

O Holy Night
(2005B)

ADOLPHE ADAM

Slowly and majestically

1. O ho - ly night! ___ the stars are bright - ly shin - ing, It is the night of the dear Sav - iour's birth; Long lay the world ___ in sin and er - ror pin - ing, Till He ap -

2. Led by the light ___ of faith se - rene - ly beam - ing, With glow - ing hearts by His cra - dle we stand; So led by light of a star ___ sweet - ly gleam - ing, Here came the

3. Tru - ly He taught us to love ___ one an - oth - er; His law is love, and His gos - pel is peace; Chains shall He break, for the slave ___ is our bro - ther, And in His

peared and the soul felt its worth.
wise men from O - ri - ent land.
name all op - pres - sion shall cease.

A thrill of hope the
The King of Kings lay
Sweet hymns of joy in

wea - ry world re - joi - ces, For yon - der breaks a new and glo - rious morn;
thus in low - ly man - ger, In all our tri - als born to be our friend;
grate - ful cho - rus raise we, Let all with - in us praise His ho - ly name;

1st time through refrain is sung by solo voice, 2nd time, four part.

Fall on your knees, Oh, hear the an - gel voi - ces! O
He knows our need To our weak - ness is no stran - ger. Be -
Christ is the Lord Oh, praise His name for - ev - er! His

night ___ di - vine, ___ O night ___ when Christ was born! O
hold ___ your King, ___ be - fore ___ Him low-ly bend! Be -
pow'r ___ and glo - ry ev - er-more pro-claim! His

night ___ O ho - ly night O night di - vine!
hold ___ your King ___ be - fore Him low-ly bend!
pow'r ___ and glo - ry ev - er-more pro-claim!

night O ho - ly night, O night di - vine!
hold your King ___ be - fore Him low-ly bend!
pow'r and glo - ry ev - er-more pro-claim!

This Old Hammer

(2202B)

SOUTHERN WORK SONG
Arr. by Charles F. Bryan

With a slow, even drag

1. This ol' ham-mer, __ uh! Jump-in' ham-mer, __ uh!
2. Night is fall-in' __ uh! All a-round us, __ uh!
3. Boss man's com-in', __ uh! Hear him run-nin', __ uh!

This ol' ham-mer, __ uh! Driv-in' ham-mer, __ uh!
Night is fall-in' __ uh! All a-round us, __ uh!
Boss man's com-in', __ uh! Hear him run-nin', __ uh!

This ol' ham-mer, __ uh! Mean ol' ham-mer, __ uh!
Night is fall-in' __ uh! All a-round us, __ uh!
Boss man's com-in', __ uh! Hear him run-nin', __ uh!

Killed poor John, __ but it won't kill me.
Ain't no rest-in' __ till the judg-ment day.
Boss man's com-in', __ but he won't find me.

Cape Cod Chantey

(2202B)

EARLY NEW ENGLAND CHANTEY

LEADER — ALL

1. Cape Cod girls they have no combs,
2. Cape Cod boys they have no sleds,
3. Cape Cod men they have no sails,
4. Cape Cod wives they have no pins,

Heave a-way, heave a-way;

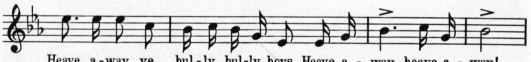

LEADER — ALL

They comb their hair with cod-fish bones,
They slide down-hill on cod-fish heads,
They sail their boats with cod-fish tails,
They pin their gowns with cod-fish fins,

We are bound for Aus-tra-lia.

Heave a-way, ye bul-ly, bul-ly boys, Heave a-way, heave a-way!

Heave a-way and don't ye make a noise, We are bound for Aus-tra-lia.

Old Chisholm Trail
(2204A)

COWBOY SONG

Lively

1. Oh, come a-long, boys, and lis-ten to my tale,
2. With a ten dol-lar hoss and a for-ty dol-lar sad-dle,
3. Oh, it's ba-con and beans most ev-'ry day,
4. With my knees in the sad-dle and my hat in the sky,

I'll tell you all my trou-bles on the old Chis-holm Trail,
I'm a-rid-ing on the trail with the Tex-as cat-tle,
I would-n't mind a change to prai-rie hay,
I'll still punch cat-tle in the sweet by and by,

Come-a ti yi yip-py yip-py yay yip-py yay,

Come-a ti yi yip-py yip-py yay.

Night Herding Song
(2004A)

COWBOY SONG

Quietly, with slow movement

1. Go slow, lit-tle do-gies, stop mill-ing a-round, For I'm
2. Lay down, lit-tle do-gies, and when you've laid down, You can

tired of your rov-ing all o-ver the ground, There's grass where you're stand-in'
stretch your-selves out, for there's plen-ty of ground. Stay put, lit-tle do-gies,

So feed kind o' slow, And you don't have for-ev-er to be on the go,
For I'm aw-ful tired, And if you get a-way I am sure to be fired,

Move slow, lit-tle do-gies, move slow. Hi-o, hi-o,—hi-o.—
Lay down, lit-tle do-gies, lay down. Hi-o, hi-o,—hi-o.—

We-We-We
(Indian Lullaby)

(2201B)

CHIPPEWA LULLABY

Very gently

We we we we we We we we we

we we we We we we we we we we we.

Rig-a-Jig-Jig

(2201A)

AMERICAN FOLK SONG

As I was walk-ing down the street, down the street, down the street,

A lit-tle friend I chanced to meet, Heigh-O, heigh-O, __ heigh - O. __

Rig-a-jig-jig and a - way we go, a - way we go, a - way we go,

Rig-a-jig-jig and a - way we go, Heigh-O, heigh-O, __ heigh-O. __

Little Bird, Go Thru My Window

(2201A)

SOUTHERN MOUNTAIN
FOLK SONG

1. Lit-tle bird, lit-tle bird, go thru my win-dow, Lit-tle bird, lit-tle bird, go
2. Blue bird, blue bird, go thru my win-dow, Blue bird, blue bird, go

thru my win-dow, Lit-tle bird, lit-tle bird, Go thru my win-dow And
thru my win-dow, Blue bird, blue bird, Go thru my win-dow And

buy mo-las-ses can-dy. Go thru my win-dow my sug-ar lump, Go
buy mo-las-ses can-dy. Go thru my win-dow my lit-tle bird, Go

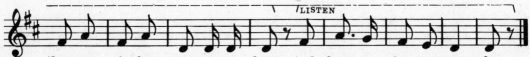

thru my win-dow my sug-ar lump, And buy mo-las-ses can-dy.
thru my win-dow my lit-tle bird, And buy mo-las-ses can-dy.

Go In and Out the Window

(2201A)

AMERICAN SINGING GAME

1. Go in and out the win-dow, Go in and out the win-dow,
2. Go forth and choose your part-ner, Go forth and choose your part-ner,

Go in and out the win-dow, As we have done be-fore.—
Go forth and choose your part-ner, As we have done be-fore.—

Corn Stalk Fiddle

(2202A)

Adapted from TENNESSEE FOLK SONG
By Charles F. Bryan

1. We got no fid-dle and we got no bow, It makes no dif-f'rence for we ought to know
2. Oh, come on fel-lows and a-way we'll go, We've got our fid-dle and we've got our bow,

The best ol' play-in' we'll ev-er know, Corn-stalk fid-dle and a shoe-string bow.
So play it fast and play it slow, Corn-stalk fid-dle and a shoe-string bow.

Corn-stalk fid-dle and a shoe-string bow, Best ol' fid-dle in the coun-ty, Oh!

Choose your part-ner and a - way we'll go, Corn-stalk fid-dle and a shoe-string bow!

Jimmy Crack Corn

(2201B)

Freely, as in speaking

EARLY MINSTREL SONG

1. When I was young I used to try to please ol' mas-sa then so spry,
2. An' when he ride in de aft-er-noon, I fol-low wid a hick-'ry broom,
3. Ol' mas-sa gone, now let him rest, Dey say all things am for de best,

lively tempo

I'd fetch the wa-ter when he got dry, And brush a-way de blue-tail fly.
De po - ny be - ing ver - y shy when bit-ten by de blue-tail fly.
I nev-er for-get till de day I die Ol' mas-sa an' de blue-tail fly.

Jim-my crack corn an' I don't care, Jim-my crack corn an' I don't care,

Jim-my crack corn an' I don't care, Ol' mas-sa's gone a - way.

Tee Nickel, Tee Nackel

(2202A)

TENNESSEE FOLK SONG
From J. B. Lasater,
Watertown, Tenn.
Collected by George Boswell

With two pulses per measure

1. I bought my wife an old milk cow,
2. — When she churned She churned in a boot, Tee nick-el, tee nack-el, tee new, new, new,
3. The but-ter she made was a griz-zle-dy grade,

She laid a-round and let her go dry,
The but-ter she made was noth-ing but soup, We'll have a see-wal-la-cy,
It set three days and walked a-way,

John-ny ding dou-ble, tee nick-el, tee nack-el, tee new, new, new.

Little Turtle Dove

(2203A)

LONESOME BALLAD
As sung by Mrs. L. L. McDowell
Smithville, Tenn.
Collected by George Boswell
Acc. by Charles F. Bryan

Slowly, smoothly

1. Don't you see yon tur-tle dove that flies from vine to vine?
2. Fare you well, my own true love, so fare you well for a-while!
3. Who will shoe your feet, my dear, and who will glove your hand?
4. Fa-ther'll shoe your feet, my dear, your moth-er'll glove your hand,

A-mourn-ing for its lost true love just like I mourn for mine.
I'm goin' a-way but I'll come a-gain, If I go ten thou-sand miles.
And who will kiss your sweet ru-by lips, While I'm in a for-eign land?
And I will kiss your sweet ru-by lips, When I re-turn a-gain.

Green Coffee Grows on White Oak Tops

(2202A)

PLAY PARTY GAME
From Mrs. Leslie Lawrence
Rutherford County, Tenn.
Collected by George Boswell

With slow walking movement

Green cof-fee grows on white oak tops, and the riv-er flows with bran-dy. —

Go choose some-one to roam with you as sweet as 'las - ses can-dy. —

Quickly

Four in the mid-dle and two walked out, Four in the mid-dle and two walked out,

Four in the mid-dle and two walked out, Swing those girls a - round you.

DIRECTIONS:

An even number of boys form a circle around the same number of girls. Holding hands, the boys circle around the girls during the slow part. For quick movement, each boy swings his own partner.

Then the girls circle the boys similarly.

NOTE:

This Tennessee folk song stems from a time when each cook bought green coffee beans and roasted them to suit her taste before grinding them. For many southern families during the Civil War, the only source for "coffee" was the acorns from the white oak.

A Paper of Pins
(2202A)

ANSWER BACK SONG
from the Cumberland Plateau
As sung by Charles Bryan
Some stanzas from Mrs. L. L. McDowell

With easy swing

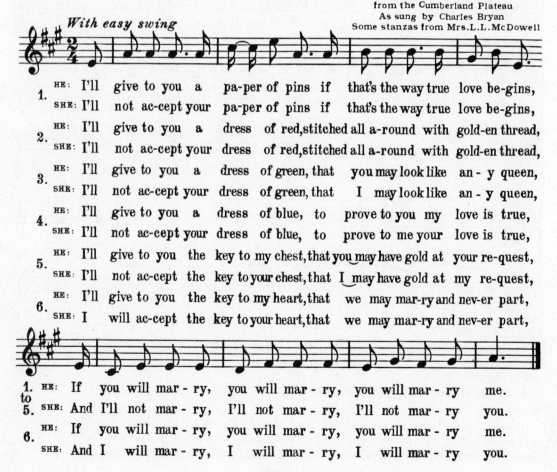

1.
HE: I'll give to you a pa-per of pins if that's the way true love be-gins,
SHE: I'll not ac-cept your pa-per of pins if that's the way true love be-gins,

2.
HE: I'll give to you a dress of red, stitched all a-round with gold-en thread,
SHE: I'll not ac-cept your dress of red, stitched all a-round with gold-en thread,

3.
HE: I'll give to you a dress of green, that you may look like an-y queen,
SHE: I'll not ac-cept your dress of green, that I may look like an-y queen,

4.
HE: I'll give to you a dress of blue, to prove to you my love is true,
SHE: I'll not ac-cept your dress of blue, to prove to me your love is true,

5.
HE: I'll give to you the key to my chest, that you may have gold at your re-quest,
SHE: I'll not ac-cept the key to your chest, that I may have gold at my re-quest,

6.
HE: I'll give to you the key to my heart, that we may mar-ry and nev-er part,
SHE: I will ac-cept the key to your heart, that we may mar-ry and nev-er part,

1.
to
5.
HE: If you will mar-ry, you will mar-ry, you will mar-ry me.
SHE: And I'll not mar-ry, I'll not mar-ry, I'll not mar-ry you.

6.
HE: If you will mar-ry, you will mar-ry, you will mar-ry me.
SHE: And I will mar-ry, I will mar-ry, I will mar-ry you.

246

Barbary Allen

(2203B)

ANGLO-AMERICAN BALLAD
Accompaniment by Charles F. Bryan

With slow, even pulse accompaniment

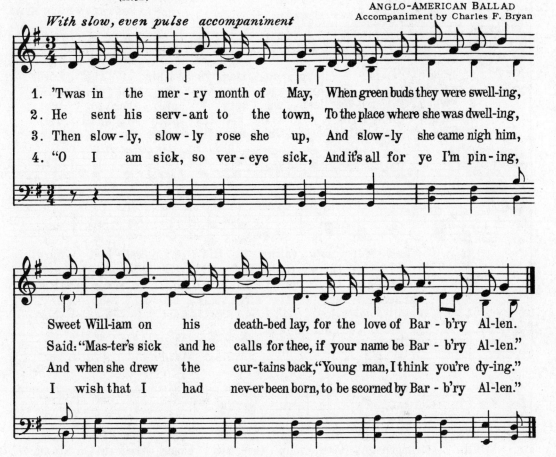

1. 'Twas in the mer-ry month of May, When green buds they were swell-ing,
2. He sent his serv-ant to the town, To the place where she was dwell-ing,
3. Then slow-ly, slow-ly rose she up, And slow-ly she came nigh him,
4. "O I am sick, so ver-eye sick, And it's all for ye I'm pin-ing,

Sweet Will-iam on his death-bed lay, for the love of Bar-b'ry Al-len.
Said: "Mas-ter's sick and he calls for thee, if your name be Bar-b'ry Al-len."
And when she drew the cur-tains back, "Young man, I think you're dy-ing."
I wish that I had nev-er been born, to be scorned by Bar-b'ry Al-len."

5. "O dinna ye mind, young man," said she, "When the red wine ye were filling,
Ye drunk the health of all around, but ye slighted Barb'ry Allen."

6. He turned his face unto the wall, and death was with him dealing,
"Adieu, adieu, my good friends all, and be kind to Barb'ry Allen."

7. As she was going through the field, she heard the death bell tolling,
And ev'ry taw the death bell gave, said: "O woe to Barb'ry Allen."

8. "O mother, mother, make my bed, O make it long and narrow,
Sweet William died for me today, I'll die for him tomorrow."

9 They buried her in the old church yard, and buried him beside her,
And from his grave there grew a rose, and from hers grew a briar.

10. They grew and grew to the old church top, 'til they could grow no higher,
And there they twined in a true-lover's knot, the rosewood and the briar.

247

How Firm a Foundation

(2205A)

SOUTHERN FOLK HYMN

Two sturdy pulses per measure

1. How firm a foun - da - tion, ye saints of the Lord,
2. "Fear not, I am with thee, O be not dis - mayed;
3. "When through the deep wa - ters I call thee to go,
4. "When through fier - y tri - als thy path - way shall lie,
5. "The soul that on Je - sus still leans for re - pose,

Is laid for your faith in His ex - cel - lent Word!
For I am thy God, and will still give thee aid;
The riv - ers of woe shall not thee o - ver - flow;
My grace, all suf - fi - cient, shall be thy sup - ply,
I will not, I will not de - sert to his foes;

What more can He say than to you He hath said,
I'll strength-en thee, help thee, and cause thee to stand,
For I will be with thee thy trou - bles to bless,
The flame shall not hurt thee; I on - ly de - sign
That soul, though all hell should en - deav - or to shake,

To you who for ref - uge to Je - sus have fled?
Up - held by My right-eous, om - nip - o - tent hand.
And sanc - ti - fy to thee thy deep - est dis - tress.
Thy dross to con - sume, and thy gold to re - fine.
I'll nev - er, no, nev - er, no, nev - er for - sake!"

Goin' Over Jordan

(2205A)

WHITE SPIRITUAL
FROM THE SOUTHERN APPALACHIANS
Accompaniment by Charles F. Bryan

Quietly, with gentle rhythm

1. I'm just a - go - in' o - ver Jor-dan, I'm just a - go - in' o - ver home,
2. I'm just a - go - in' o - ver Jor-dan, I'm just a - go - in' o - ver home,
3. I'm just a - go - in' o - ver Jor-dan, I'm just a - go - in' o - ver home,

I'm just a - go-in' o - ver Jor-dan, I'm just a - go - in' o - ver home.
Where I'll be free from toil and sor-row, Where I will rest, no more to roam.
Where I shall meet my heav'n-ly fa-ther, Where I shall claim my heav'n-ly home.

I'm go-in' there to see my fa-ther, I'm go-in' there no more to roam,
I'm go-in' there to see my moth-er, I'm go-in' there no more to roam,
I'm go-in' there to meet my Sav-iour, I'm go-in' there no more to roam,

Slowing

I'm just a - go-in' o - ver Jor-dan, I'm just a - go - in' o - ver home.
I'm just a - go-in' o - ver Jor-dan, I'm just a - go - in' o - ver home.
I'm just a - go-in' o - ver Jor-dan, I'm just a - go - in' o - ver home.

The Barbadoes Lady

(2203B)

ANGLO-AMERICAN BALLAD
As sung by Charles F. Bryan

With rolling movement

1. The Bar-ba-does la-dy, the Bar-ba-does la-dy,___
2. Says: now if you fan-cy a Bar-ba-does la-dy,___
3. Whilst he was a-sail-ing on back to old Eng-land,___
4. At dead of the night when the whole world was sleep-ing,___
5. O yes, dear-est Nan-cy, I am your true lov-er;___

The Bar-ba-does la-dy, her for-tune was great.___
A Bar-ba-does la-dy whose for-tune is great.___
She wrote a short note to the bo'-s'n, her friend,___
At Nan-cy's high win-dow a voice she did hear,___
And, dead or a-live, I know you are my own.___

She fix-ed her eyes on a young Eng-lish sail-or;___
Says: now if you fan-cy a Bar-ba-does la-dy,___
Says: hand-some re-ward I will pres-ent-ly give you,___
Says: rise you up now, I am here, pret-ty Nan-cy,___
It's for your true prom-ise that now I am su-ing;___

Says: if I don't get him he'll die for my sake.___
Then you shall have mu-sic to charm you to sleep.___
And if you the life of young Jem-my will end.___
And true to my vows that I made to my dear.___
So fol-low me down to the wa-ter-y tomb.___

She dress'd her-self up in her rich-est at-tire,___
Then Jem-my, he said to the Bar-ba-does la-dy:___
Be-cause of her mon-ey, be-cause of her beau-ty,___
She raised up her head from her soft down-y pil-low,___
O yes, dear-est Jem-my, I'll soon be a-go-ing,___

With cost - li - est dia - monds she plat - ted her hair.____
A Bar - ba - does la - dy is hard to de - ny,____
Whilst they were a - lone and young Jem - my did sleep,____
And soon at her case - ment she then did ap - pear.____
And soon I will lie on your bos - om a - sleep.____

A hun - dred of slaves then she took to wait on her;____
But back in old Eng - land I've vowed to my Nan - cy,____
Whilst they were a - lone and were sail - ing to - geth - er,____
The moon it was bright and so clear it was shin - ing;____
No soon - er had this most un - hap - py girl spo - ken,____

And with her two maid - ens she went to him there.____
That on my re - turn I would make her my bride.____
The bo' - s'n he tum - bl'd him in - to the deep.____
That sure - ly must be the sweet voice of my dear.____
She plung'd her - self sud - den - ly in - to the deep.____

THE MEANING OF MUSICAL TERMS AND SYMBOLS

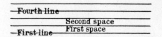

The *Staff*, on which notes are placed to show their pitch, has five lines with spaces between. Where the round part of the note is placed on the staff tells us its pitch, that is, how high or low it will sound. Lines and spaces are both used. For example, second space is one note higher in the scale than second line.

The notes on the staff really make a picture of the way the tune goes; the way it sounds.

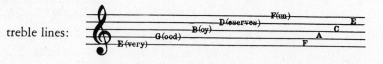

Si - lent night   A - way down south in Dix-ie

Brace. Whenever one five-line staff is joined with another staff by a vertical brace at the left margin, we know that the music of both staffs happens together, at the same time. So when we finish that line and come back to the left for the next, we must move down the page to the next brace.

The *Clef sign* gives definite pitch meaning to the lines and spaces. The *G clef*, or treble clef, locates the G above middle C on the *second line*. The staff with G clef is used for treble voices, soprano range instruments, and notes for the right hand in piano music.

The *F clef*, or bass clef, locates the F below middle C on the fourth line. This staff is used for bass or baritone voices and instruments, and notes for the left hand in piano music.

Pitch Names of Lines and Spaces
(First seven letters of the alphabet)

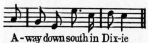

Jingles to help remember

treble lines: 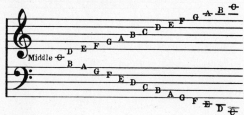   treble spaces

bass lines: 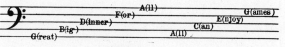   bass spaces

THE MEANING OF MUSICAL TERMS AND SYMBOLS

Key Signature. The sharps (♯) or flats (♭) with the clef sign at the beginning of the staff help us to know the key of the piece and show us the location of the keynote on the staff. The keynote is the center, or the "home base," of the key. It is the important foundation tone in the key chord and very often is the final note of the song. In major keys the tone name of the keynote is *do*. In minor, the keynote is *la*.

Locating do (or 1) from the Key Signature

In major when there are no sharps or flats in the signature, the key is C and *do* (1) is located on C.

When there are sharps in the key signature the last sharp, located farthest to the right, is for *ti*, seventh tone of the scale, just a half step below *do;* so it is easy to find the *do* location on the next line or space up.

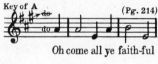

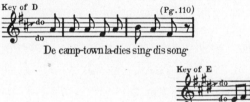

When there are flats in the key signature, the last flat to the right is for *fa*, fourth tone of the scale. When there are more flats than one, *do* is located easily because the next-to-the-last flat is for *do* and therefore names the key.

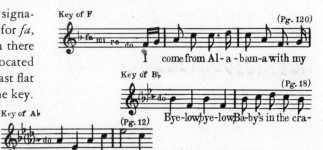

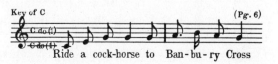

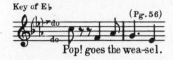

Accidentals. When music needs a tone which is not part of the key indicated by the key signature, an *accidental* is used to show the change in pitch. A *sharp* (♯) in front of a note means the tone is a half step higher than in the regular pattern of the key. A *flat* (♭) means the tone is a half step lower. A *cancel* (♮) , or natural, cancels out the effect of a sharp or flat which otherwise would apply. If it cancels a sharp in the key signature the tone is lowered a half step. If it cancels a flat, the tone is raised a half step. An accidental applies only in the measure where it is used and affects only the note(s) on that same line or space.

THE MEANING OF MUSICAL TERMS AND SYMBOLS

The Measure Signature, which often looks like a fraction just to the right of the key signature, tells us two things which work together. The upper number tells how many pulses or counts per measure. The lower number shows what kind of a note receives one count. For example, $\frac{3}{4}$ means $\frac{3}{\quarternote}$. There are *three* counts per measure, so the music will go with a feel of | one-two-three | one-two-three | etc., and a quarter note (♩) is the kind of note for one pulse or count. Together, $\frac{3}{4}$ means that in this song each measure will have three quarter notes | ♩ ♩ ♩ | or notes equal to that:

$$| \quarternote \quad \quarternote \quarternote | \quarternote \quarternote \eighthnote\eighthnote | \quarternote. | \quarternote. \eighthnote\quarternote | \text{ etc.}$$

Compound Measure. When the upper number of the measure sign is 6, as in $\frac{6}{8}$ or $\frac{6}{4}$, the six counts naturally divide into two groups of three, and the movement has a feeling of two strong pulses per measure. Another way to show the meaning of $\frac{6}{8}$ is $\frac{2}{(\quarternote.)}$, which says there are two pulses per measure and the dotted quarter note (♩.) is the amount of each pulse.

There are two measure signatures, or time signs, that do not use figures like a fraction. (1) 𝄴 means $\frac{4}{4}$. (2) 𝄵 means $\frac{4}{4}$ going fast enough to feel *two* pulses or steps per measure instead of four. It is equal to $\frac{2}{2}$ but with a rather quick movement as in marching.

Notes and Rests Compared   whole,   half,   quarter,   eighth,   sixteenth

(note)   o   ♩   ♩   ♪   ♬

(rest)   ▬   ▬   𝄽 or 𝄾   𝄿   𝅀

Time Values Compared   A dotted note is longer; it is half again as long as a similar note without a dot.

| o | = | ♩♩ | = | ♩ ♩ ♩ | = | ♩. ♩ | = | ♩♩— |

| ♩ | = | ♩♩ | = | ♪♪♩ | = | ♪𝄾 ♫ | = | ♩. ♪ |

| ♩ | = | ♪♪ | = | ♫ | = | ♪ 𝄾 | = | ♬♬ | = | ♪♪♪ |

| ♩. | = | ♩ ♩ | = | ♩♩♩ | = | ♩ 𝄽 ♩ |

| ♩. | = | ♪♪♪ | = | ♩ ♪ | = | ♩ 𝄾 | = | ♪. ♪♪ |

Changes of Tempo

accel. (accelerando)—Gradually increasing speed
rit. (ritardando)—⎱ Gradually
rall. (rallentando)—⎰ slowing
poco rit.—A little slowing
a tempo—In time (usually after a slowing)
meno—Less
meno mosso—Less movement, slower
piu—More
piu mosso—More movement, faster
stringendo—Quickening, as toward a climax

Tempo (time)—Rate of Movement

In order from slow to fast:
largo—Very slow, broad
lento—Slow
adagio—Slow (at ease)
andante—Like walking
moderato—Moderate
allegretto—Rather quick
allegro—Quick
presto—Very fast
prestissimo—As fast as possible

THE MEANING OF MUSICAL TERMS AND SYMBOLS

Dynamic—Degree of Loudness

pp (pianissimo)—Very soft

p (piano)—Soft

mp (mezzo piano)—Half soft

mf (mezzo forte)—Half loud

f (forte)—Loud

ff (fortissimo)—Very loud

sf (sforzando)—Sudden, strong accent on a single tone or chord

cres. (crescendo) ◁—Gradually increasing in loudness

decresc. (decrescendo) } Gradually

dim. (diminuendo) } softening ▷

Terms of Expression

animato—Full of life

cantabile—Singing, melodious

con brio—With fire

con moto—With motion

dolce—Sweetly

giocoso—Playful, in fun

grazioso—Graceful

legato—Connected

leggiero—Very light

maestoso—With majesty

molto—Much, very

poco—Little

poco a poco—Little by little, gradually

staccato—Very detached, disconnected

vivace—Lively, very spirited

Signs That Direct Us

D.C. (Da Capo)—Go back to the beginning and sing or play again, this time as far as the end (*Fine*).

D.S. (Dal Segno)—Go back to the sign and sing or play again, this time to the end (*Fine*).

𝄋 (Sign) Sing or play again from here.

𝄇 (Repeat) Go back as far as the other repeat sign 𝄆 and sing or play again. But when you look back, if there is no other repeat sign with dots on the right of the bar, repeat from the beginning.

⌐1⌐ Sing or play this part now; but when you repeat, skip this part and take second ending, marked: ⌐2⌐

⌢ (fermata)—Hold; keep singing or playing longer than the note value.

♩. | ♩ (tie)—Sustain as long as the two notes added together.

♩ ♪ ‿ (slur)—Sing both notes on the same word in the text.

, —(breath mark)—Take breath here, to phrase nicely.

♪ ♪ ♪ ³ —(triplet)—Sing or play these three evenly but in the usual time for two.

8v ——— (octave sign, placed above the staff)—Play an octave higher than written.

Follett Educational Records

The following songs are available on records
from FOLLETT PUBLISHING COMPANY, Chicago

ALBUM 1

ALBUM 2

ALBUM 3
Charles A. Fullerton Memorial Album

FOLLETT EDUCATIONAL RECORDS

ALBUM 21
Patriotic Songs

RECORD	TITLE	PAGE
2101B	America	211
2103B	America, the Beautiful	209
*2104A	Anchors Aweigh	
*2102B	Army Air Corps Song	
2104B	Battle Hymn of the Republic	210
2102B	Caissons Go Rolling Along	217

RECORD	TITLE	PAGE
2104A	Columbia, the Gem of the Ocean	220
2103A	Dixie Land	212
2104B	God of Our Fathers	223
2102A	Home Road, The	222
2102A	Hymn for the Nations	201
2105B	Marines' Hymn, The	216

RECORD	TITLE	PAGE
2101A	Star-Spangled Banner, The	214
2105B	Taps	217
2105A	Thanksgiving Prayer	188
2105A	When Johnny Comes Marching Home	218
2103A	Yankee Doodle	219

*Words and Music available only as sheet music.

ALBUM 22
American Folk Songs

RECORD	TITLE	PAGE
2202B	Away for Rio	122
2203B	Barbadoes Lady, The	248
2203B	Barbary Allen	247
2204B	Beautiful Dreamer	152
2202B	Cape Cod Chantey	239
2203A	Cindy	129
2202A	Corn Stalk Fiddle	243
2203A	Frog Went A-Courting	118
2204B	Glendy Burk, De	154
2201A	Go In and Out the Window	242
2205A	Goin' Over Jordan	251
2201A	High, Betty Martin	30

RECORD	TITLE	PAGE
2202A	Green Coffee Grows on White Oak Tops	245
2204A	Home on the Range	126
2205A	How Firm a Foundation	250
2201B	Jimmy Crack Corn	243
2201A	Little Bird, Go Through My Window	242
2203A	Little Turtle Dove	244
2201B	My Little Owlet	69
2204A	Night Herding Song	240
2205B	Nobody Knows the Trouble I See	176
2204A	Old Chisholm Trail	240

RECORD	TITLE	PAGE
2204B	Old Folks at Home	191
2202A	Paper of Pins, A	246
2201B	Paw Paw Patch	75
2201B	Pop Goes the Weasel	56
2201A	Rig-a-Jig-Jig	241
2205B	Rise Up, Shepherd, and Foller	230
2202A	Tee Nickel, Tee Nackel	244
2201A	This is Mother's Knives and Forks	30
2202B	This Old Hammer	238
2201B	We-We-We (Indian Lullaby)	241

Classified Index

CLASSIFIED INDEX

CLASSIFIED INDEX

CLASSIFIED INDEX

CLASSIFIED INDEX

CLASSIFIED INDEX

Alphabetical Index

ALPHABETICAL INDEX

ALPHABETICAL INDEX

ALPHABETICAL INDEX

11121314151617181920696867665